3

Animal Population Ecology

Animal Population Ecology

J. P. DEMPSTER

Institute of Terrestrial Ecology,
Monks Wood Experimental Station,
Abbots Ripton, Huntingdon

1975

ACADEMIC PRESS
London   New York   San Francisco

A Subsidiary of Harcourt Brace Jovanovich, Publishers

ACADEMIC PRESS INC. (LONDON) LTD.
24/28 Oval Road,
London NW1

United States Edition published by
ACADEMIC PRESS INC.
111 Fifth Avenue
New York, New York 10003

Library of Congress Catalog Card Number: 75 11374
ISBN 0 12 209550 2 X

PRINTED IN GREAT BRITAIN BY
PAGE BROS (NORWICH) LTD, NORWICH

Preface

One cannot work in a subject for twenty years without developing one's own set of prejudices. One of mine is that I believe that a real understanding of the factors determining the abundance of animals can be obtained only by the intensive study of animal populations in the field. In my opinion, only limited progress can be made in constructing realistic population models until there is a firmer basis of field data on which to build. I have little doubt that this bias will be readily recognisable in this book, but I should like to think that this will encourage students to study real situations rather than to build elaborate theories for which the basic assumptions cannot be tested. The latter is an attractive past-time, since it avoids the need for committing many years to the collection of data. On the other hand, population ecology suffers from a surfeit of theories and a scarcity of hard evidence. Added to this, considerable satisfaction can be obtained from trying to unravel the complex of factors which affect an animal's numbers, and there are many problems facing Man today which can be solved only by an understanding of the dynamics of animal populations. I have no hesitation in recommending population ecology as a worthwhile and challenging subject for study. I hope that I have managed to convey some of its excitement in this short book.

March, 1975   J P Dempster

Acknowledgements

It gives me pleasure to thank my wife and my colleagues at Monks Wood for their helpful criticism of earlier versions of this manuscript. In particular, I wish to acknowledge the help given to me by Mrs Marney L King at all stages in the preparation of this book, and especially for drawing the figures which I have used.

I am most grateful to the following people for permission to copy tables and figures which have been previously published.

Table XVI: Dr D A Hancock and the Centre for Agricultural Publishing and Documentation, Wageningen.

Figs 6 and 18: Professor G C Varley, Dr M P Hassell and the British Ecological Society.

Fig 10: Dr R H Watmough and the British Ecological Society.

Figs 11 and 14: Dr M P Hassell and the British Ecological Society.

Fig 13: Dr C S Holling and the Entomological Society of Canada.

Figs 17 and 43: The Royal Entomolgical Society of London and Blackwells Scientific Publications, Oxford.

Fig 19: The British Trust for Ornithology.

Fig 20: The British Ecological Society.

Fig 31: Professor G C Varley and the British Ecological Society.

Figs 49 and 50: Dr J. A Gulland and the Centre for Agricultural Publishing and Documentation, Wageningen.

Contents

1. Introduction

All species of animal have evolved in communities of other animal and plant species. Each community tends to occur within a particular type of habitat, since the requirements of individual species are often precise and different species are dependent upon one another for food and shelter. These natural complexes of plant and animal species, together with the physical and chemical conditions under which they live are called "ecosystems" (Tansley, 1935). Although individual species may occur in a number of similar ecosystems, each ecosystem has its own characteristic flora and fauna. Thus the term salt-marsh ecosystem identifies the functional system involving the plant and animal populations and the climatic and edaphic conditions which occur in a salt-marsh habitat. Thus any one species tends to live in a characteristic biotic, chemical and physical environment to which it is adapted by evolution.

Ecosystems are, or tend to become, relatively constant states of existence in which the numbers of the component species fluctuate within certain circumscribed limits. The interaction between the environment and the population of each species determines the extent of these fluctuations and this interaction forms the basis for the subject "Population Ecology". Population ecology is then the study of the factors which determine the abundance of species. It is concerned with the identification and mode of action of those environmental factors which cause fluctuations in population size and of those which determine the extent of these fluctuations.

The words "population" and "environment" are both in general usage, and so it is perhaps useful at this stage to define what a population ecologist means by these terms. A number of definitions have been

1

published for both terms (Clark *et al.*, 1967), but in this book the following meanings will be used.

A population is a group of organisms of the same species separated, more or less clearly in time or space, from other groups of the same species. All species are patchy in their distribution, so that all occur in more or less distinct populations which are separated by uninhabited areas. Animal populations are rarely discrete entities however, since individuals may move from one population to another. Provided that the amount of such movement is small, or is measurable, a population may be treated as a unit for which such characteristics as birth-rate, death-rate, age-structure, genetic make-up, density and dispersion can be determined.

The environment may be defined as the sum total of factors which influence the number of individuals within a population. The environment includes those physical, chemical and biotic factors which are affecting the survival and multiplication of individuals. It will be noted that this definition is in terms of effects upon individual animals, not upon their total population. The reason for this is that other individuals in a population are themselves part of the environment, since population density affects both survival and multiplication rates. The environment determines the trend in population size through its effects upon individuals within the population. This is comparable to the action of natural selection, which operates on individuals, but which determines the course of evolution of species.

The interaction between the various factors which affect an animal's numbers makes it difficult to present the subject in a linear sequence of chapters. For this reason, I have dealt with the subject in four main sections. Chapter 2 describes some of the basic ideas about animal populations and defines many of the terms used by population ecologists. Chapters 3–7 describe the action of the most important factors affecting population size, while the interaction between these factors is demonstrated in Chapters 8–9, in which the results from studies of a few selected species are described in detail. Lastly, the development of generalized theories of population dynamics and their application to practical problems are discussed in the light of our present knowledge (Chapters 10–11).

Man has long been interested in animal numbers, because of his exploitation of some species for food and because of his need to control other competing pest species. The development of population ecology as a science has been slow, however. This is primarily due to two reasons. First, the working-life of an ecologist tends to be short compared with the time scale of natural changes. It is unlikely that he can study more than twenty generations of a univoltine species and this may be too few to fully understand the fluctuations in its numbers. Secondly, the numbers of any one species are affected by a large complex of factors and at best, an ecologist can usually measure only part of this complex. The biotic part of an animal's environment is composed of a web of interactions involving many different species (enemies, competitors and food organisms). Within this web, the levels of dependence between different species will differ enormously. Superimposed upon this is the variability in the physical and chemical environment brought about by changes in weather. The result is a complexity which is difficult to unravel in the field and impossible to simulate in laboratory experiments.

The past forty years have seen a series of theories developed to explain animal numbers. These have frequently been based more on dogma than on reliable field evidence, so that population ecology has passed through a turbulent period of controversy. Only now are the results from field studies reaching a stage when some of these theories can be tested. It would be unfair to say that population theory has restricted the development of the subject, since it has produced many fruitful ideas, but it is certainly arguable that population ecologists have been too preoccupied with theory in the past.

This book attempts to review the present state of our knowledge of the population dynamics of animals. Many of the conclusions which are made must be tentative and there is little doubt that some will be proved wrong by future research. It is hoped that this book will stimulate more research in this subject by attracting attention to the gaps in our knowledge. As a research subject it has much to offer, since it combines the fascination of understanding natural phenomena with the intellectual satisfaction of unravelling extremely complex relationships. It is a subject in which simple natural history observation and highly sophisticated techniques of quantitative biology and mathematics can each play a part.

2. Some Basic Concepts

Populations are usually changing continually under the impact of environmental factors which affect birth- or death-rates. In order to explain these changes in population size we must be able to describe rates of growth or decline quantitatively, and for this, we need to be able to measure population gains and losses. Gains occur from reproduction and from immigration, while losses occur from mortality and emigration. Before discussing these in detail let us first look at be overall powers of increase of animal populations.

I. Rates of Population Growth

In the highly hypothetical situation of unrestricted growth, the growth-rate of an animal population is exponential or geometric (Fig. 1). Geometric increase generates a straight line slope when numbers are graphed on a logarithmic scale against time. In other words, the relationship between log N (population) and t (time) is linear and the slope of the line is r, when r equals births minus deaths. Thus,

$$\frac{dN}{dt} = rN.$$

The parameter r describes the rate of population growth in an ideal, unlimiting environment. If the population has a stable age distribution, r is a constant and is known as the "potential rate of increase" of the population. The need for a stable age distribution is obvious, since age affects both reproduction and mortality rates. Most species do not reproduce before or after a certain age and death-rates are also dependent upon age. Generally the greater the number of generations which overlap in time, the more stable will be the age distribution of the population.

Unrestricted growth is of course an unrealistic concept, since all natural environments will limit population increase in some way. A more realistic concept is the maximum value of r which is possible for a species under the influence of a particular environment. This is generally called the "intrinsic or innate rate of increase" and is usually denoted

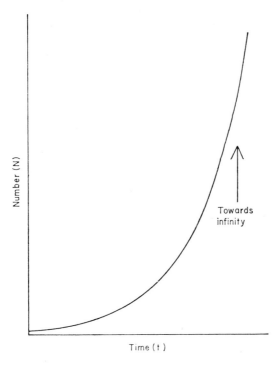

Fig. 1: Exponential Population Growth.

by the symbol r_m. The calculation of intrinsic rate of increase of a population under given conditions is useful as a description of growth potential and for comparisons between species; but it must be remembered that the environmental factors (climatic, biotic, etc.) which are operating, must be described when giving the value of r_m.

Exponential growth of a population is unlikely ever to last for long even in the most constant environment, because lack of food, space, or some other requirement will always ultimately limit population size. As the population approaches the carrying capacity of the habitat the rate of increase will decline. A more realistic model of population growth is then likely to be given by the equation.

$$\frac{dN}{dt} = rN\frac{(K - N)}{K}$$

where K is the carrying capacity of the habitat, that is the maximum number that the habitat can support. The integral form of this equation

$$N = \frac{K}{1 + e^{(a-rt)}}$$

is known as the "logistic equation", and the curve for population growth obtained from the equation is called the "logistic curve" (Fig. 2). In

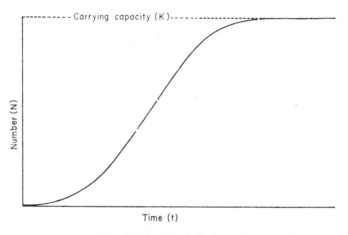

Fig. 2: The "Logistic Curve".

this equation a is the constant of integration and defines the position of the curve in relation to the origin. The logistic equation was first proposed as long ago as 1844 by Verhulst, but it has since formed the basis for many population models. It was a particularly important development in population ecology, since it was the first formulation of the concept of density-dependent growth.

Many ecologists have attempted to prove the validity of the logistic curve by simple laboratory experiment. Amongst the most famous of these were the experiments of Gause (1934) on two species of *Paramecium* (*P. aurelia* and *P. caudatum*). Gause attempted to rear *Paramecium* in as constant an environment as possible, but in a limited space. Twenty

Paramecium were placed in 5cc of buffered salt solution (Osterhaut's medium) and a constant quantity of the bacterium *Baccillus pyocyaneus* (now called *Pseudomonas deruginosa*) was introduced from a pure culture as food. When added to the salt solution they did not multiply, so that the quantity of food available to the *Paramecium* was known. The tubes were kept at a constant temperature of 26°C and every second day the culture was washed with bacteria-free medium to reduce the accumulation of waste products. In other words, temperature, chemical composition, volume and food supply were kept roughly constant. The number of *Paramecium* was estimated each day by removing a small sample (0·5cc) of the culture. The results obtained roughly fitted a logistic curve (Fig. 3). A large part of the scatter of points about the lines is probably due to sampling errors in the estimation of the numbers present.

The theory of the logistic curve involves the assumption that the population has a stable age structure which remains unaltered during the growth of the population. None of the experiments which have been done to test the theory has met this requirement. The main reason for this is that extremely large populations would be required to have a stable age structure. There is no way of knowing precisely how this will affect the final results, but one would expect the effect to be smallest in species like *Paramecium* in which the non-reproductive stages occupy little of the life cycle and greatest in species in which the immature stages occupy a relatively large part of the life cycle. In practice, the more complicated has been the life cycle of the animal studied, the less well has the logistic curve described the experimental results. Besides this requirement that the population has a stable age distribution, the logistic curve will only describe population growth if the effect of density on the rate of increase is linear and instantaneous, that is with no time lag.

Although the fit may often be imperfect, the logistic curve does give a useful description of the growth of experimental populations in a constant environment, but in limited space. In a variable environment however, it will not hold, since rate of growth will be influenced by an array of factors and the supply of such requirements as food is unlikely ever to be completely unaffected by the size of the population.

The logistic curve demonstrates how population growth can be dependent upon population density. As the population nears the carrying capacity of the habitat its rate of growth declines. This may be due to increased mortality (or emigration) or to reduced reproduction (or immigration). As we shall see below, all of these may depend upon population density.

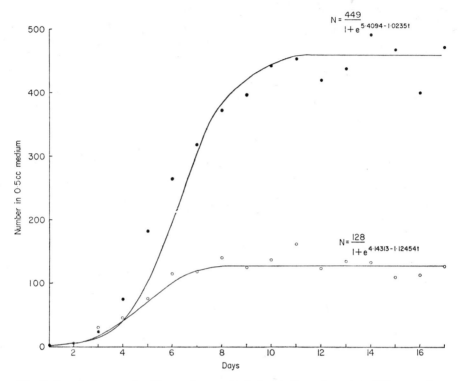

Fig. 3: Population trends of *Paramecium aurelia* (●) and *P. candatum* (○). The smooth curves are logistic curves calculated from the data (Gause, 1934).

II. Birth-rates and Death-rates

A. Effects of Age

Most animals have a long period of growth before starting to reproduce, and most do not reproduce after a certain age. In long-lived species the pattern of births and deaths may be sufficiently constant to produce a stable age structure for the population. In short-lived species with complex life cycles this will not be so, and in these, variations in the age of individuals in the population will greatly alter birth-rates.

Age also influences rates of mortality. If the logarithm of the number of survivors is plotted against age, three basic types of curve can be obtained (Fig. 4) (Deevey, 1947). A straight line (curve A) implies a constant rate of mortality through life, that is a no greater probability of dying at one age than at another. This rather unlikely situation appears to apply to many species of bird. Lack's (1943) data for the lapwing (*Vanellus vanellus* (Fig. 5)) excludes the first eleven weeks, or

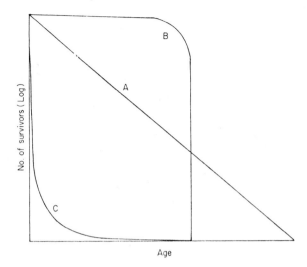

Fig. 4: The three basic types of survivorship curve.

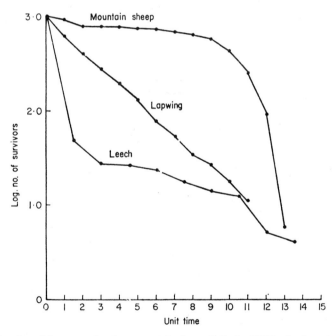

Fig. 5: Survivorship curves for the mountain sheep (Murie, 1944), the lapwing (Lack, 1943) and the leech, *Glossiphonia* (Mann, 1957).

so, after ringing. Earlier mortality would probably have been far higher.

A convex curve (B in Fig. 4) indicates a very low mortality throughout life until old age, when death occurs over a short period of time. Man is nearest to this situation, but Murie's data for mountain sheep (Murie, 1944) roughly fit this type of curve (Fig. 5).

A concave curve (C) indicates a very high number of deaths during early life and few after a certain age. This is the commonest type of survivorship curve met with in animals; most invertebrates and lower vertebrates show this pattern of mortality. For example, a female cod (*Gadus morhua*) may lay as many as a million eggs, but most of her progeny will be dead before the end of their first year. An example of this type of curve is shown in Fig. 5 for the leech *Glossiphonia complanata* (Mann, 1957).

There is a tendency for the higher vertebrates to have more convex survivorship curves, due to the greater parental care to their offspring. The more protection given to the young, the more convex the curve becomes (Deevey, 1947; Itô, 1959, 1961).

B. Effects of Density

The most obvious effect of density on birth-rate is when overcrowding creates a shortage of food, or some other requirement, and this results in a reduced fecundity. Examples of this are given in Chapter 3. The effects of density can be far more subtle than this however, and in some

Table I. The rate of multiplication of *Aphis fabae* reared at different densities (all differences sigificant at 5% level) (*Way*, 1968)

Initial No. adults per plant	Multiplication rate during first 8 days of reproduction
2	× 29
4	× 41
8	× 46
16	× 36
32	× 27

species there is an optimum density above and below which reproduction is impaired. Way (1968) gives an example of this for *Aphis fabae* (Table I). This aphid has its highest rate of multiplication at a density of about eight adults per bean plant. Above this density overcrowding begins but below this density reproduction is also reduced. The reason for this is that group feeding by this species enhances the movement of nutrients to the feeding site on the plant. A group of less than eight individuals is too small to have this effect.

Mortality may also be related to density in a number of ways. It may be "density-dependent", that is to say, a higher proportion of the population may die from a particular cause at high densities. It is not enough for the number of deaths to increase as density increases; there must be an increase in the percentage dying for a mortality factor to be density-dependent. Death from starvation may in some cases be an example of density-dependent mortality (see Chapter 3).

Some mortality factors show some delay before reaction to density. For example, some natural enemies become abundant one generation after a peak in the numbers of their prey, as a result of better survival and reproduction on the abundant supply of food. Such factors are described as "delayed density-dependent" (Varley, 1947). Their overall effect will be complicated and will depend upon the length of the delay in reaction (see p. 51).

A smaller proportion of the population may be killed at high than at low densities, when the mortality factor is described as being "inversely density-dependent". We shall see an example of this when we look at the effect of some natural enemies on the populations of their prey (Chapter 6).

Lastly, if a mortality factor is unrelated to population density, it is referred to as "density-independent".

III. Dispersal

The term "dispersal" covers any movement of individuals away from a population. Animal species differ considerably in their powers of dispersal. Some may actively fly, swim or walk large distances from their original habitat; others may depend entirely on movements of air, water or other organisms for transport. Most animals however, are capable of some movement and many species have an innate tendency for dispersal, often at a particular stage in their life cycle. This may occur at almost any stage in their development. Species, such as barnacles and certain molluscs, with sessile adults, disperse in their early larval stages.

Spiders and some insects which disperse on the wind, also do so as larvae. Many insects disperse by flight and therefore do so as winged adults, but even these tend to disperse for a relatively short period, often as an immature adult (Johnson, 1960, 1963). Many birds and mammals also tend to disperse as immature adults. Age can then have considerable effects upon rates of dispersal and periodic dispersal by particular age groups can involve a large part of some populations.

Dispersal forms an essential part of the way of life of some animals, particularly those inhabiting temporary habitats (Southwood, 1962). The main evolutionary advantage of migration lies in it enabling a species to keep pace with changes in the location of suitable habitats. Dispersal may be obligatory for these animals, but for others it is facultative and is triggered off by unsatisfactory conditions. Overcrowding can act in this way, so that dispersal may be density-dependent. This is discussed more fully, with examples, in Chapters 3 and 5.

IV. Natural Control

When one considers the huge potential rate of increase of some animals, their adult numbers tend to fluctuate surprisingly little from generation to generation. The factors which are responsible for the restriction of fluctuations in number are known collectively as "natural control". Solomon (1964) defines natural control formally as "the process(es) keeping numbers of animals in a population not controlled by man, within the limits of fluctuation observed over a sufficiently representative period".

Some ecologists use the term "regulation" loosely to mean natural control, but I prefer to restrict its use to control by density-dependent processes, in the way suggested by Nicholson (1933, 1954). He believed that populations exist in a state of balance with their environments, as a result of density-dependent opposition to indefinite population growth. He referred to such factors as density-governing (= density-dependent); that is those factors which intensify their opposition to population growth as numbers increase, eventually preventing further growth, and which relax their opposition as numbers decrease. Control by density-dependent factors in this way he called population regulation. I believe that Nicholson's concepts of balance and of regulation are unrealistic (see Chapter 10), but they are accepted by many ecologists and so the terms are in frequent use. The two concepts, "natural control" and "regulation" (in the Nicholsonian sense), are quite different. Regulating factors will tend to cause the population to return to an equilibrium density whenever the environment causes it to increase or decrease. Natural control, on the other hand, will simply set limits on population growth, thus damping fluctuations.

V. Animal Life Tables

We have so far described populations in terms of their rates of increase and of their survivorship curves. By far the best way of understanding the population dynamics of a species however, is by the construction and analysis of "life tables". Life tables have long been used by actuaries for determining the expectation of life of applicants for insurance. In the case of human populations, life tables can be built up from censuses in which the entire population is enumerated on a fixed day, once every ten years or so. Added to this, information is available on birth-rates (from the registrar of births) and on the proportions of people dying at different ages (from the registrar of deaths).

In the case of animal populations, it is rarely possible to study the entire population and only rarely can individuals be aged with any certainty. For these reasons, the development of life tables for animals has taken a somewhat different line to that used by actuaries.

There are basically two types of life table used by animal ecologists. First there is the "time-specific" (static, current, or vertical) life table, and secondly, there is the "age-specific" (cohort, generation, or horizontal) life table. These two types of life table differ in form and in meaning. The time-specific table is calculated on the basis of a cross section of the population at a specific time. It presents such population parameters as average mortality and average expectation of life for each age class. The age-specific table, on the other hand, is calculated on the basis of a single cohort of animals, usually one generation, for which deaths are recorded in each age class. The two types of life table would be identical only if the environment did not change the age-structure and size of the population from generation to generation. As it is, however, there are normally good and bad years for any population.

A. Time-specific Life Tables

For some animals, the age at death is directly observable for a large and reasonably random sample of the population. For example, the skulls of some large animals can be aged, or the death of ringed birds can be associated with age. In other cases, the age structure of the population can be assessed by aging live individuals, as with fish. Death-rates can then be inferred from the shrinkage between successive age-classes.

Life tables can be built up from these data to give a concise summary of the statistics of the population (Southwood, 1966). Such tables usually

Table II. Showing the usual form of a time-specific life table

x	l_x	d_x	q_x	e_x	L_x	T_x
1	1000	550	550	1·21	725	1210
2	450	250	556	1·08	325	485
3	200	150	750	0·80	125	160
4	50	40	800	0·70	30	35
5	10	10	1000	0·50	5	5

take the form shown in Table II, in which the statistics are listed under five columns. In this:

x = age class;

l_x = number surviving at the beginning of the age interval out of 1000;

d_x = number dying in the age interval out of 1000;

q_x = mortality per thousand alive at the beginning of the age interval $(1000 \cdot dx/lx)$;

and e_x = expectation of life.

In practice, the table may include two further columns to facilitate the calculation of e_x. First,

L_x = number of individuals between age x and $(x + 1)$.

If the age interval is not long,

$$L_x = \frac{l_x + l_{(x+1)}}{2}.$$

Secondly, T_x = total number of individuals of age x and beyond.

$T_x = L_x + L_{(x+1)} + L_{(x+2)}$, etc.

Then,
$$e_x = \frac{T_x}{l_x}.$$

The stages in this calculation become clearer if one realizes that for any age (x), expectation of life is equal to the area under the survivorship curve beyond x, divided by the number of survivors attaining age x. At birth this equals the mean length of life of individuals in the population.

A time-specific life table can be used only if the population has a stable age distribution. For this reason it is more appropriately used for animals with a considerable overlap between generations, such as long-lived mammals. This type of life table gives one an average picture of mortality and recruitment. It will not provide realistic information for species which have very variable annual birth- and death-rates. For this reason a time-specific life table is of rather limited usefulness in studies of the effects of the environment upon population trends. This type of table is useful, however, when assessing the optimum sustainable yield from populations of animals exploited by Man, examples of which are to be found in Chapter 11.

B. Age-specific Life Tables

For many animals, such as most insects, recruitment and mortality may vary enormously between different generations. For this type of animal a series of age-specific life tables provide far more information than a time-specific table.

An age-specific life table usually lists the actual population in different age classes and records the action of mortality factors where these are known. In order to simplify the calculation of life expectancy some workers prefer to start each generation with a fixed number of individuals, e.g. 1000. This means however, that important information on actual population size is lost. An example of the more typical form of an age-specific life table is shown in Table III for the cinnabar moth (*Tyria jacobaeae*).

Age-specific life tables can be used only with animals for which the survival of a large cohort (born more or less simultaneously) can be followed at fairly close intervals throughout life. This approach is statistically more satisfactory than the time-specific life table, provided the number of individuals entering the cohort can be accurately assessed.

In order to understand the effect that any one environmental factor has on the trend of a population, a series of age-specific life tables is required covering a number of generations. The analysis of a series of this sort enables one to assess the effect of each component of the environment. A number of different techniques have been used to analyse life-table data (c.f. Southwood, 1966). One method in particular is now widely used, namely, the "*k*-factor analysis" of Varley and Gradwell (1960). Since this is the method used in Chapters 8 and 9, a brief description of the technique is given here.

The technique of *k*-factor analysis enables one to recognize:

1. the "key-factor or factors" determining population trend, that is those factors which give the best prediction of numbers in future generations;
2. the effect of variations in natality and mortality on the population;
3. the recognition of any density-dependent relationships which exist.

Table III. Age-specific life table for *Tyria jacobaeae* in 1967

Age class	Cause of change in numbers	No. entering stage	No. dying	% dying	% initial number dying (accum'd)
Adult	Fecundity (285·2 eggs per female)	109 (55% ♀♀)			
Egg	Infertility	17110	189	1·1	
	Failure to hatch		161	0·9	
	Miscellaneous		516	3·1	
				5·1	5·1
Larva I + II	Starvation	16244	772	4·7	
	Arthropod predators + unknown		9849	60·6	
				65·3	67·2
Larva III + IV	Starvation	5623	1680	29·8	
	Arthropod predators + unknown		504	9·0	
				38·8	80·0
Larva V	*Apanteles*	3439	519	15·1	
	Starvation + failure at pupation		1174	34·1	
				49·2	89·9
Pupa	Vertebrate predators	1746	1380	79·9	
	Failure at emergence + unknown		4	0·2	
				80·1	97·9
Adult		362			

The simplest way of describing this technique is to work through the life table for *Tyria* given in Table III. First, we need to calculate the maximum potential production of off-spring (natality) for each generation, that is the number of females of reproductive age multiplied by the maximum number of eggs per female (600 eggs/♀♀ for *Tyria*, Dempster, 1971). In 1967 this was

$$109 \times 0.55 \times 600 = 35,970$$

This is entered as the first figure in the table (Table IV). Next, the

Table IV. *k*–factor analysis of the data in Table III.

	Number	Log Number	*k*-value
Max potential natality	35970	4·5560	
			$0·3228 = k_0$
Eggs laid	17110	4·2332	
			$0·0225 = k_1$
Larvae hatching	16244	4·2107	
			$0·4608 = k_2$
Third instar larvae	5623	3·7499	
			$0·2135 = k_3$
Fifth instar larvae	3439	3·5364	
			$0·2937 = k_4$
Pupae	1749	3·2427	
			$0·6840 = k_5$
Adults	362	2·5587	
			$1·9973 = K$

number of each successive stage in the life cycle is entered and the values are converted to logarithms. A series of "mortalities"[1] can then be calculated by subtracting each logarithm from the previous one, i.e.

$$k_i = \log N_i - \log N_{i+1}$$

These are the *k*-values for each age class. Total generation "mortality" is given by the addition of successive *k*-values, i.e.

$$K = k_0 + k_1 + k_2 + k_3.$$

[1] *k*-value and mortality (μ) are related as follows:

$$k = \frac{1}{\log_{10}(1 - \mu)}$$

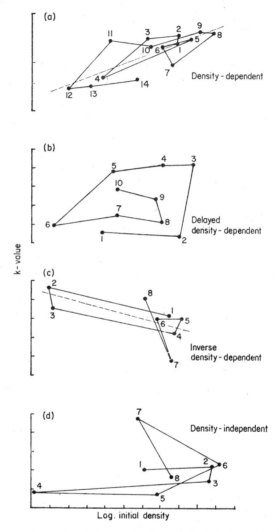

Fig. 6: Patterns produced by different density relationships. (a) Density-dependent predation on winter moth pupae (Varley and Gradwell, 1963; Hassell, 1966). (b) Delayed density-dependent predation on rock ptarmigan eggs (Weeden and Theberge, 1972). (c) Inverse density-dependent parasitism on gypsy moth eggs (Bess, 1966). (d) Density-independent predation on cinnabar moth larvae (Dempster, 1971).

k_0 is not strictly a mortality, but is the reduction in the population resulting from the failure of females to lay their full potential of eggs.

The next step is the identification of the key factor(s) which determines the trend in adult numbers from one generation to the next. This may be done visually by plotting the k-values for successive generations, when any correlation between each k and the total K can be seen. This has been done for *Tyria* in Fig. 22 (p. 77). Alternatively, correlation coefficients can be calculated. Significance tests on the correlations between K and individual k-values will not be valid, but the correlation coefficient can be used as a descriptive statistic (Smith, 1973).

Insight into the mode of action of each k-factor may be obtained by plotting each against the logarithm of the initial density on which it is acting, and joining the points in sequence. Different density relationships are then indicated by the patterns formed (Fig. 6).

The proof of density dependence is more difficult to do with any certainty. A slope of greater than zero suggests a density-dependent relationship, but regression analysis assumes a number of features to be true about the variables being tested and these assumptions are not all met by life-table data. Simple regression analysis assumes a linear relationship between the independent variable (i.e. population) and dependent variable (i.e. k-factor), and as we shall see later this may not be true (see p. 71). Secondly, it is assumed that the independent variable is free from error and this is certainly not true in population studies, since the estimates of population size normally have a sampling error. Lastly, it is assumed that the variables being tested are independent. If both initial density and mortality are determined directly, as in the case of estimates of rates of parasitism or disease, this assumption is met. More frequently, however, the calculation of the k-value (log N_i − log N_{i+1}) includes the initial population (log N_i). Detailed discussion of the difficulties in using regression analysis can be found in the following papers (Maelzer, 1970; St. Amant, 1970; Luck, 1971; Kuno, 1971; Itô, 1972; Benson, 1973a). Because of these difficulties, Varley and Gradwell (1968) recommend the following test for density dependence. If both of the regressions of initial upon final density (log N_i on log N_{i+1}) and of final upon initial density (log N_{i+1} on log N_i) produce slopes which are significantly different from a slope of $b = 1$, and are on the same side of the slope of unity (Fig. 7), density dependence may be taken as proved. In effect, this test ensures that variance about the regressions is small, since the regression lines move closer together as the correlation coefficient increases. Itô (1972) criticizes this two-way regression test on the grounds that a prediction of log N_i from log N_{i+1} is nonsense. This is true, but prediction is not the purpose of the test.

At present, this two-way regression test is the best test for density dependence which is available, provided that the relationship is linear. For final proof however, any density-dependent relationship shown by this test should be demonstrated experimentally and be shown to be biologically meaningful. Having done this the slope of the regression of k_i on N_i gives a measure of how the density-dependent factor will act. The nearer the slope is to unity, the greater compensatory effect the factor will have on density changes.

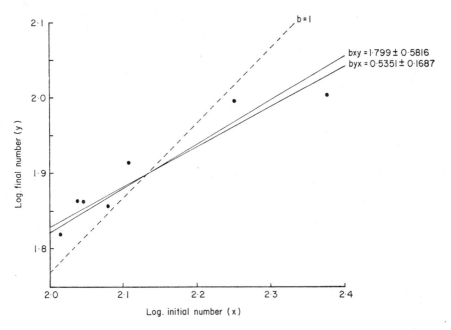

Fig. 7: The two-way regression test for density dependence. The predation of wood pigeon eggs by jays (Murton 1974a).

The k-factor analysis may be used only on univoltine species; otherwise, seasonal changes in mortality may give a false impression of the key factor(s). Attempts have been made to use this technique with long-lived species such as birds, by expressing mortalities of eggs and young in relation to the whole population at the time, including adult birds (Blank, *et al.*, 1967; Krebs, 1970; Watson, 1971; Weeden and Theberge, 1972). This is not to be recommended because adult mortality is almost certain to differ from that of eggs and young birds, and the inclusion of adults in the analysis will therefore bias estimates of mortality. This will be particularly marked in later age classes when numbers of young may be comparatively small. For most species, adult mortality is low compared with that of younger age-classes, and inclusion of adults in the analysis will damp fluctuations in the k-values obtained (see for example, Fig. 35 (p. 97) and Fig. 1 (Murton, 1974a)). The use of the k-factor technique should therefore be restricted to single cohorts of progeny, as used by Southern (1970).

The analysis of age-specific life tables by means of the k-factor techniques is the best method available at present for the study of population dynamics. Other techniques such as the construction of survivorship curves, or of time-specific life tables, are useful in giving summaries of average effects, but they do not provide a means of measuring the impact of individual environmental factors on the trend of a population from generation to generation.

3. Resources

I. Intra-specific Competition

Each species of animal has its own set of requirements from a habitat, such as food, water, space, shelter, nesting or egg-laying sites, and any one area of habitat will have a limited supply of these requisites. The maximum number of a species which a habitat can support throughout their lives is known as the "carrying capacity" of the habitat. This may vary from season to season and from year to year, but it sets a ceiling to the growth of any population through "competition" between animals for resources.

There have been many attempts to define the term "competition" (Bakker, 1961; Birch, 1957; Milne, 1961) but in my opinion that proposed by Milne is the most useful definition. He defines it as follows: Competition is the endeavour of two (or more) animals to gain a particular requirement, or to gain the measure each wants from the supply of a requirement, when that supply is not sufficient for both (or all). It is implicit in this definition that, for competition to occur, the supply of the requirement must be affected by the number of animals searching for it. In other words, one individual gaining its requirements, must reduce the chance of others doing likewise, that is competition must be density-dependent.

Williamson (1972) criticises Milne's definition on the grounds that it is based on the individual rather than the population level of organization. It is true that inter-specific competition can be usefully defined in terms of interactions between populations, in the way that Williamson suggests, but intra-specific competition is between individuals within one population and cannot be easily defined in this way. Milne's definition can be applied to competition between individuals of the same and of different species.

22

Some workers, notably Andrewartha and Birch (1954) have pointed out that a requirement may be in short supply and yet be quite unaffected by the number of animals searching for it. In this case, the shortage is simply a reflection of the poor searching ability of the animals relative to the distribution of the resource. This has led some workers to distinguish between an "absolute shortage" of a resource, which is density-dependent (i.e. when competition occurs), and a "relative shortage" which is independent of density (i.e. when competition does not occur). In practice it is extremely difficult to determine when an animal's numbers have reached a level where they start to affect the supply of a requisite, but this distinction may become clearer from the following example.

Anthocoris sarothamni is a small predatory plant-bug which lives on broom (*Sarothamnus scoparius*). It is restricted to the one host plant and it feeds mainly on two species of psyllid (*Arytaina spartii* and *A. genistae*) (Dempster, 1963a). The psyllids are extremely patchily distributed and are hidden within the overlapping scales of the buds of the plant, so that large numbers may be present without *Anthocoris* finding sufficient. In seven out of the nine generations that were studied the reproductive success of *Anthocoris* was apparently limited by lack of psyllid prey (Fig. 8) (Dempster, 1968a). In 1962 (first generation) there were only

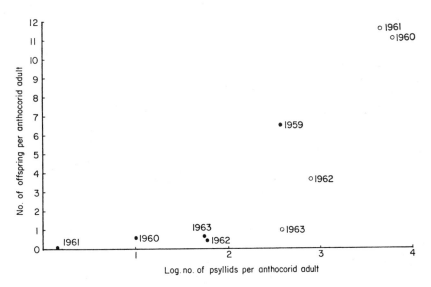

Fig. 8: The relationship between reproductive success of *Anthocoris sarothamni* and the density of their psyllid prey. ○, first generation; ●, second generation.

B

about five *Anthocoris* adults and about 4000 psyllids per bush, but the reproductive success of *Anthocoris* was low. At these densities it is very difficult to imagine that one individual *Anthocoris* finding a psyllid made any difference to the chance of another individual finding prey. In that year there was probably a relative shortage of prey, because *Anthocoris* was incapable of finding enough due to their patchy distribution. In the previous year (1961, second generation), there were eighty-seven *Anthocoris* and only 120 psyllids per bush. At this time there was almost certainly an absolute shortage of prey and competition was taking place.

The effect of competition will depend to some extent on the type of interaction which occurs between individuals within the population. Some species compete passively for their requirements; others actively contest the supply of resources. These two types of interaction are usually referred to as "scramble-competition" and "contest-competition". Scramble competition, as for example caterpillars competing for a food plant, will result in all individuals eating food until the supply runs out. In cases of extreme shortage, all individuals may obtain some food, but all may die of starvation. Contest competition will commonly result in one individual finishing up with all the food while another gets none. An example of this is two foxes competing for a dead pheasant. This type of competition is less wasteful than the scramble type, since it increases the chance that at least some individuals obtain sufficient. Less of the resource is wasted on individuals which will not obtain enough to survive.

The impact that intra-specific competition has upon a population will also depend upon the type of resource which is in short supply. Competition for a non-consumable resource, such as a territory, will have no effect on its availability in subsequent generations. On the other hand, competition for a resource such as food, may well affect the supply of that resource to later generations, since it will usually take some time for food plants, or prey organisms, to recover from the effects of over-exploitation.

Over the range of densities at which it occurs intra-specific competition will cause density-dependent mortality. At densities below this however, competition does not exist and so it can play no part in determining survival. If mortality due to intra-specific competition is plotted against density, a graph with the general shape shown in Fig. 9 is therefore obtained. Density-dependent mortality operates only above the threshold where population density starts to affect the supply of the resource. An example of this is seen for a field population of *Tyria jacobaeae* in Fig. 24 (p. 72). Benson (1963b) shows similar curves for laboratory populations of *Plodia interpunctella* and *Ephestia cautella*.

Competition not only affects mortality of individuals in a population, it also affects their reproduction. Its precise effect on reproduction will however, depend upon the type of resource which is in limited supply, and the stage of the life cycle which is overcrowded.

Shortage of a resource which is required by adults can have a direct density-dependent effect on the number of young produced. We saw one example of this with *Anthocoris sarothamni* in which food supply determined

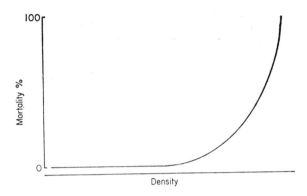

Fig. 9: The pattern of mortality resulting from intra-specific competition.

reproductive success. Another example is seen in the effect of intra-specific competition for oviposition sites by the psyllids upon which *A. sarothamni* feeds. Watmough (1968) showed that *Arytaina spartii* lays its eggs in the stems of the new growth of broom. When adult density is high, there is a shortage of suitable oviposition sites (Fig. 10), and fewer eggs are laid. Food shortage can have considerable effects on the fecundity of animals and in extreme cases can lead to complete absence of reproduction. Southern (1970) found that the tawny owl does not reproduce in years of extreme food shortage (see Chapter 8). Similarly, a shortage of psyllid prey during early adult life can cause *Anthocoris sarothamni* to enter a reproductive diapause which lasts until the following psyllid generation (Anderson, 1962).

Reproduction may also be affected by competition for food or space amongst the younger stages in the life cycle. For example, food shortage during the larval stages of many insects results in smaller, shorter-lived and less fecund adults. When this happens the effect of intra-specific competition on reproduction is delayed until the adult stage. In such cases, the number of young produced in one generation is dependent upon the population density of the previous generation and

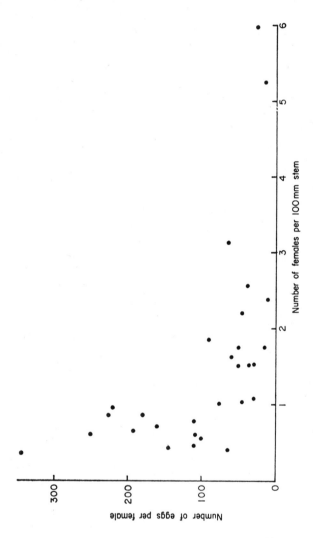

Fig. 10: The effect of density on the fecundity of *Arytaina spartii*.

competition acts as a delayed density-dependent factor. Examples of this are seen in Chapters 8 and 9.

Competition may also affect reproduction through changes in the sex-ratio. Examples of this are frequently found in parasitic Hymenoptera in which superparasitism causes increased mortality, reduced size and a reduction in the proportion of females produced (Wylie, 1966; Benson, 1973c). Benson showed, for example, that as with many parasitic Hymenoptera, female *Bracon hebetor* develop from fertilized eggs and males from unfertilized ones. When only three eggs were laid per host, approximately equal numbers of males and females were produced, but three times as many males as females were produced from eighteen eggs per host. The reason for this is that male larvae develop more quickly and are better able to survive shortage of food caused by competition at higher densities.

Overcrowding can cause an array of physiological changes in animals which are often associated with stress. Just one effect of these is to alter fecundity. Chitty's studies on the short-tailed vole (*Microtus agrestis*) demonstrates this (Chitty, 1952; 1957). He showed that there is a three or four year cycle in the numbers of this vole which is not readily correlated with any environmental factor and is out of phase in different localities. He found no evidence of food shortage at the population peaks, but the crash phase in the cycle was characterized by increased juvenile mortality, reduction in the length of the breeding season and in the fertility of females. The peaks were characterized by increased fighting and territorial behaviour, and at this time the thymus, spleen and adrenal glands became enlarged. Chitty described this as a self-regulating mechanism by which the vole population was never allowed to reach the size when food becomes a limiting factor (see Chapter 10). One has however, only to consider space as a requisite to explain Chitty's findings solely in terms of intra-specific competition. Overcrowding brings about a complex array of changes in the voles which affects both survival and reproductive rates.

There is considerable disagreement amongst ecologists as to how frequently intra-specific competition occurs in wild populations. Milne (1957b) for example, believes that it is only on rare occasions that competition between individuals within a population ever occurs. It is this idea that most species never reach numbers approaching the carrying capacity of their habitat, and the fact that some species have evolved conventional goals of competition, such as territory or social status, that has led other ecologists (e.g. Wynne-Edwards, 1962; Way and Cammell, 1971) to suggest methods of self regulation of populations (see Chapters 4 and 10). There are two factors which give a false, superficial impression that competition rarely occurs. First, it is often difficult to assess the carrying capacity of a habitat without detailed knowledge of the requirements of a species, and these are often very much more precise than at first appears. Secondly, most animals respond to unfavourable conditions, such as overcrowding, by dispersing. This means that intraspecific competition may be an extremely transient condition which is easily overlooked, since the population density may immediately be reduced by emigration.

To illustrate the first of these, when one is looking at a meadow, it is difficult to imagine that food can ever be a limiting resource to a grass-feeding insect. On the other hand, a stem-boring dipteran, such as *Oscinella frit*, can only attack grass tillers of the right age, since its larvae must be capable of penetrating the shoot. This means that it can exploit only a relatively small number of the millions of grass stems which are present in the meadow.

It is not always food which is the limiting resource: other requirements, such as shelter from weather or from enemies, egglaying, nesting or hibernation sites, may be in short supply. The more complicated a life cycle an animal has, the more complex are its requirements likely to be. Without a knowledge of these, one can have a very false impression of the carrying capacity of a habitat.

There has been a considerable amount of research on dispersal in animals, but very few attempts have been made to study the effects of population density on the proportion of a population dispersing. One of the reasons for this has been the difficulty of obtaining data on immigration/emigration rates. There is however, a growing body of information which suggests that intra-specific competition greatly increases the proportion of a population which disperses. Two examples of this can be seen from the study of *Anthocoris sarothamni* and *Arytaina spartii* (Dempster, 1963a, 1968a; Watmough 1968). During the five years of this study a suction trap was operating continuously about 100 yd from the broom plantation (50 yd in 1959). The nearest other area of broom was about a quarter of a mile away and contained few bushes, and there is little doubt that most of the individuals of *A. spartii* and *Anthocoris sarothamni* caught in this trap originated from the study area.

Table V shows the number of *Arytaina spartii* caught in this suction trap during May and June in each year. The number caught was exceedingly high in 1961 and it is clear that there was a considerable emigration of adults from the study area in that year. During the 15 days when adults were found in the suction trap, numbers dropped from 7800 to 1100 per bush on the study area (Watmough 1968). Fecundity was also extremely low in that year and although no estimate was made

Table V. Fecundity and Mobility of *Arytaina spartii* adults

	Peak No. of adults/bush	Fecundity $\left(\dfrac{\text{No. of eggs}}{\text{Peak No. adults}}\right)$	Suction Trap Catch	$\left(\dfrac{\text{No. trapped}}{\substack{\text{Peak No.}\\ \text{adults/bush}}}\right)$
1959	316	—	118	0·37
1960	3880	146·3	850	0·22
1961	7792	6·4	10572	1·36
1962	223	267·5	131	0·59
1963	74	—	26	0·35

of the availability of young, green shoots for oviposition, this was certainly lower than in any other year of the study. Owing to the very high numbers of *Arytaina* nymphs in that year, many buds failed to produce a shoot at all, while very many more produced only stunted growth which was unsuitable for egg-laying. There is little doubt that there was a shortage of oviposition sites in 1961 and that this led to the reduced fecundity and mass emigration of adults in that year.

Psyllid numbers crashed in 1961 and between June and August in that year higher numbers of *Anthocoris* were caught in the suction trap than in any other year (Table VI). We have seen that the reproductive

Table VI. Mobility of *Anthocoris sarothamni* adults

	No. psyllids per *Anthocoris* at time of flight	No. *Anthocoris* trapped	$\dfrac{\text{No.trapped}}{\substack{\text{Mean No.}\\ \text{adults/bush}}}$
1959	377	2	0·80
1960	14	6	0·34
1961	1	29	1·55
1962	60	2	0·67
1963	57	1	0·50

success of *Anthocoris* was abnormally low in 1961, due almost certainly to intra-specific competition for prey (see p. 23). This also appears to have caused an emigration of *Anthocoris* in that year. As one would expect with any mobile animal, both *Arytaina* and *Anthocoris* did not stay to die, but emigrated in search of their requirements.

Intra-specific competition occurs regularly in populations of some species in some localities. Other populations of the same species in other localities may rarely reach densities where competition occurs (see Chapter 8). The carrying capacity of any habitat is not static but is continually changing in response to such environmental factors as weather, seasons, other species of animal, etc., and intra-specific competition may be brought about by changes in the carrying capacity of the habitat, as well as by variations in population size. This is particularly true for those animals living in habitats which show large seasonal changes.

II. Inter-specific Competition

Inter-specific competition may occur when two or more species require the same resource, and this resource is in limited supply. When this happens, one species may have such a large effect upon the carrying capacity of the habitat that it greatly reduces the upper limit to which the population of another species can grow. We will see in Chapter 8, that some populations of the cinnabar moth (*Tyria jacobaeae*) completely defoliate their food plants in some years. When this happens, this moth greatly reduces the availability of food for other species feeding on the same plant.

There have been a number of laboratory studies of inter-specific competition under controlled conditions (Gause, 1934; Crombie, 1945; Park, 1948; Birch, 1953). Many of these experiments have produced similar results, namely, that when two species share the same limited resource and all other environmental factors are kept constant, one species dies out. Under any one set of environmental conditions one species has an advantage over the other and will eliminate it. Under a different set of conditions however, the other species may predominate. Birch (1953) found for example, that in mixed cultures of *Calandra oryzae* and *Rhizopertha dominica*, *Rhizopertha* became extinct at 29°C, but *Calandra* did so at 32°C. *Calandra* had the higher innate capacity for increase at 29°C, whilst that of *Rhizopertha* was highest at 32°C.

The elimination of one species by another is far less likely to occur in wild populations, since the varying environment will give an advantage first to one species, then to another. In this way several species may share the same resource, but all may be able to persist under field conditions.

Inter-specific competition must occur commonly in natural populations, but well documented examples are difficult to find. Reynoldson and Bellamy (1971) describe a good example from their work on planarians (Tricladida). They showed that the natural colonization of a lake in Anglesey by *Polycelis tenuis* led to a decline in the population of *Polycelis nigra* which had previously inhabited the lake alone. After six or seven years the total *Polycelis* population was approximately un-changed, although *P. tenuis* had almost replaced *P. nigra*. Survival and reproduction of the two species in cages suspended in the shallow water of the lake showed that the habitat was still favourable for *P. nigra* at the end of the period.

In Britain, four species of planarians commonly inhabit the shallow littoral waters of lakes with stony shores; the two species of *Polycelis*, *Dugesia polychroa* and *Dendrocoelum lacteum*. All four species are predatory and there is a wide overlap in their diets (Reynoldson and Davies, 1970). Each species tends however, to feed more heavily on a particular type of prey. *Dendrocoelum* which is the biggest and most active predator, takes more Crustacea, particularly *Asellus*, than the other species. Simi-larly, *Dugesia* takes more gastropods (snails), while the two species of *Polycelis* feed most heavily upon oligochaete worms. Reynoldson and Bellamy (1971) suggest that each species of *Polycelis* has a specific prey preference within the oligochaetes but more work is required to identify this.

All four species appear to live under conditions of extreme food shortage for long periods of the year, especially during the summers when large numbers of young are present. At these times, many individ-uals die of starvation, but all four species have the ability to resorb their tissues during periods of food shortage, so that individuals shrink in size, but can recover again when food becomes available. Each summer, the existence of intra-specific competition was indicated by the small size, low proportion of adults, and low fecundity in field populations compared with samples provided with ample food in the laboratory. Field experiments also showed the existence of intra-specific competition. Symptoms of competition were removed by artificially increasing the food supply, or by reducing the population size prior to the onset of breeding (Reynoldson and Bellamy, 1971).

Lakes of low productivity have smaller populations and fewer species of triclad than high productivity lakes. *Polycelis nigra* tends to occur alone in the poorest lakes (measured by calcium content and total dissolved matter in the water), but all four species coexist in the richest lakes. This suggests that these triclads compete with one another in un-productive waters where the variety of prey is more restricted.

Inter-specific competition for a resource is unlikely ever to occur without intra-specific competition occurring at the same time. For this reason its precise effect on any one species will be difficult to quantify. Inter-specific competition will increase mortality and reduce repro-duction, but these changes are unlikely to be density-dependent for any one species, since the supply of the resource will be affected by both (or more) competing species. Far more quantitative work is required on competing populations in the field, however, before the impact of inter-specific competition can be fully understood.

III. Under Population

Group feeding is commonly found throughout the animal kingdom and some species, such as *Aphis fabae* (see p. 11), are incapable of efficient exploitation of their food resource at very low densities. Similarly, individuals of the sawfly, *Neodiprion banksianae,* differ in their ability to break through the cuticle of pine-needles, but when once a feeding site has been established several larvae can make use of it (Ghent, 1960). For this reason, survival within small groups of larvae is better than for isolated individuals. By hunting in packs many predators can overpower prey which are too large for them to tackle individually. Many species of bird are more efficient at searching for food when feeding in flocks (e.g. the wood-pigeon, *Columba palumbus*; cf. p. 36). For these species there is an optimum group size for the most efficient exploitation of their food. This has led some ecologists to suggest that survival and reproduction may be reduced by under population in relation to a resource (e.g. Browning, 1968). In practice this is probably unimportant in affecting population trends, since even very low populations can form optimum sized groups by aggregation.

4. Social Behaviour

The role played in the natural control of animal populations by such phenomena as territorial behaviour and dominance hierarchies has been a subject of controversy for many years. Some ecologists believe that an animal can regulate its own numbers below the carrying capacity of its habitat by social behaviour of this sort. This idea of "self-regulation" has become sufficiently widely accepted to warrant its treatment here in a separate chapter, away from other aspects of intra-specific competition. Clearly, if self-regulation is possible it will enable an animal to avoid the harmful effects of competition.

I. Territorial Behaviour

Many species of animal defend an area or "territory" against other individuals of the same species. Individuals, pairs or groups of animals may hold territories for varying periods of time, from a few hours to many years. Although territorial behaviour is most commonly found amongst the vertebrates, it also occurs in a number of invertebrate animals, such as dragonflies (Moore, 1964) and butterflies (Baker, 1972; Shields, 1967). The purpose of territoriality almost certainly differs with different types of animal. In many insects it may be linked with the finding of a mate, since males defend their territories against other males, and attempt to mate with any virgin female which enters the area. In other animals territory is linked with food supply, while other species will hold a territory only during breeding seasons. In these, the size of the territory held by a pair varies enormously between different species. Thus colonial nesting sea-birds may defend an area immediately around their nests, to a distance that can be reached by a sitting bird. Other

33

birds, on the other hand, may defend a very large area within which the pair will nest and feed. In any one species there is probably an optimum territory size which an individual can defend without expending an uneconomic amount of energy, but which is large enough to fulfil the function of the territory.

It is not always easy to understand the purpose of territory. Sometimes the spacing of individuals within a population is clearly linked with competition for food, or space for foraging for food. Recher and Recher (1969) describe an example of this among western sandpipers (*Calidris mauri*) and sanderlings (*Crocethia alba*). When flocks of these birds are feeding on inter-tidal mudflats, each bird shows aggressive behaviour to other individuals of the same species and drives them from the immediate area around which it is feeding. This is clearly an extension of the contest type of intra-specific competition for food (described on p. 24), to include a foraging area.

The advantage of holding a territory for breeding is less easy to understand. A number of possibilities exist. The defence of a territory around the nesting site may assist in pair formation and may ensure safe breeding and lack of disturbance from other individuals of the same species. It may ensure an adequate food supply for the young. It may also improve survival, since spacing out of the nests may conceal them from predators, and perhaps reduce the spread of disease. Lastly, it is possible that territoriality plays an important part in population regulation.

This last suggestion dates back fifty years to Howard (1920), but the idea has more recently been extended by Wynne-Edwards (1962) in his book "Animal Dispersion in Relation to Social Behaviour". It is easy to see why this idea has developed, since at first sight, territorial behaviour appears to set an upper limit to the number of breeding pairs in an area. When density is high a smaller proportion of the population obtains a territory and breeds. As has been pointed out by several workers however (e.g. Brown, 1969; Lack, 1966) the evidence that territorial behaviour actually does limit population size is far from conclusive.

Brown (loc. cit.) points out that the effects that territoriality has on a population will depend upon the population density. At low densities, territorial behaviour ensures a mosaic pattern of dispersion, but no individuals will be prevented from breeding through lack of a territory. At a higher density, some individuals may be forced to breed in less favourable areas. Krebs (1971) describes an example of this sort for great tits (*Parus major*). He showed that territorial behaviour limited the number of pairs breeding in his woodland, and forced some birds to nest in the surrounding hedgerows, where reproductive success was lower. At an even higher density, all available territories may be occupied and some individuals are prevented from breeding, that is, there is a surplus of potential breeders. At this density, territory, like any other resource, is in short supply and is limiting population size. A surplus of potential breeders must be demonstrated for this to be proved however, and evidence for this is frequently lacking.

Many workers have tried to show the existence of a non-breeding surplus by removing territory holders to see whether they are replaced by other individuals. Frequently these experiments have been inconclusive because birds of only one sex, usually males, have been removed and this does not show whether there is an excess of females. On the other hand, removal experiments have shown that there regularly is a non-breeding surplus of adults in some species. An example of this is seen in the red grouse (*Lagopus lagopus scoticus*), for which there existed a non-breeding surplus of birds every year during a five-year study (Jenkins *et al.*, 1967). In this species, however, the number of territories held varied enormously between years. This was due to variations in the average aggressiveness of cock birds and possibly to changes in the quality of their food supply (see Chapter 9). In other words, territorial behaviour did not lead to a stable breeding density in the red grouse.

Lack (1966) suggested that birds modify the size of their territories in accordance with the supply of food, but attempts to correlate the size of breeding territories with the food situation have produced mixed results. In some species, territory size varies little from one year to another, although food supply may fluctuate considerably. As we shall see in Chapter 8, territory size is very constant in the tawny owl (*Strix aluca*), but food supply can be so inadequate in some years that no breeding occurs. In contrast, Lockie (1955) showed that there was a relationship between territory size and food supply in the short-eared owl (*Asio flammeus*). In years when their principal prey (*Microtis agrestis*) was scarce, many owls emigrated and those remaining held very large territories. It is not clear however, whether territorial behaviour limited the numbers breeding (i.e. determined the numbers emigrating), or whether it merely spaced out those which remained after food supply had determined the numbers (Lack, 1966).

Clearly far more work requires to be done to determine the function of territory in different species. In my opinion however, it is becoming clear that territorial behaviour does not in itself limit population density. On the other hand, territory may sometimes be a limiting resource, in which case, it is intra-specific competition for that resource which limits population size.

II. Social Hierarchies

Animals which live or feed in groups frequently develop a social hierarchy in which some individuals are dominant over others. In its simplest form the top individual dominates all others, the second ranking individual dominates all except the top individual, and so on in a linear series, or peck order. Frequently, the hierarchy is a good deal more complicated than this with groups of individuals showing equal dominance over others. Individual status may depend upon such things as age, sex, rank of mate, or reproductive state. Normally, once rank is established, usually by a period of fighting, it is no longer contested. Fighting is then rare and is replaced simply by threat. Recognition of social status is advantageous to both dominant and subordinate individuals since it avoids the need for repeated fighting.

Social organization within groups is commonly associated with dominance with respect to feeding. This again is simply an extension of the contest type of intra-specific competition, except that threat has removed the need to fight. In this way the higher ranking individual obtains food with very little fighting, and the lower individual avoids a fight which it would only lose anyway, and so can spend more time searching for food elsewhere. The disadvantages of feeding in a group for subordinate individuals must presumably be outweighed by some advantage of group feeding. The work of Murton *et al.* (1971) on the wood pigeon (*Columba palumbus*) suggests that this is so. In winter, this pigeon feeds in flocks in which there develops a marked dominance hierarchy. Young inexperienced birds tend to be subordinate and these tend to frequent the front of the flock. In this way they can see and copy the feeding behaviour of older, more experienced birds (Murton, 1971). On the other hand, in this position they are continually being harassed by more dominant individuals. If density is high in relation to food supply, subordinate birds are unable to feed successfully and are forced to leave. It was found that solitary birds obtained even less food per unit time than subordinate individuals in a flock, since they fed only sporadically and spent much of their time looking around as if afraid of being surprised by a predator. In other words it was advantageous for an individual to feed in a flock even if it was low in the social hierarchy.

In some mammals high ranking animals are not only dominant with respect to feeding, but also in other ways, including breeding. This is well illustrated by some primates. For example, subordinate male baboons (*Papio cynocephalus*) frequently mate with females during the beginning of their oestrus cycle, but when the female becomes fully fertile she mates only with the dominant males. Consequently, most of the offspring are sired by the dominant males (De Vore and Hall, 1965).

Wynne-Edwards (1962) asserts that the population size of some animals is limited below the level of starvation by substituting conventional goals of competition, such as territorial rights and social status, in place of any direct contest for food itself. These ideas, and the problems which would be involved in the evolution of conventional goals will be discussed in Chapter 10. We have seen (p. 35) that there is little evidence that territorial behaviour limits population density, although intra-specific competition for the resource, territory, may do so. Just how territory is linked with food supply, if at all, is uncertain, but in some species (e.g. tawny owl) possession of a territory does not ensure that food supply will be adequate, i.e. food supply can still limit population growth in spite of territorial behaviour.

Similarly, social hierarchies do not prevent intra-specific competition for food, but simply ensure that the successful competitors get enough for their needs. In this way the more wasteful scramble-type of competition, and the need for serious fighting, are both avoided.

5. Qualitative Changes in Individuals

Qualitative changes in individuals which are correlated with changes in the density of their populations have been recorded for many animals. Basically, these changes fall into three types. First, there are the changes brought about by the harmful effects of intra-specific competition. These have been discussed in Chapter 3. Secondly, there are a number of instances in which insects undergo density-dependent changes which appear to be linked with dispersal, for example, "phase" changes in locusts. Lastly, there are changes in the genetic make-up of populations which are caused by a relaxation of natural selection during periods of population expansion. In this chapter we shall be looking at the last two of these.

I. "Phase" Changes in Insects

Qualitative changes of this sort have been found in a number of insects when they are living under crowded conditions (Uvarov, 1961; Gruys, 1970). They have been most thoroughly studied in locusts (Acrididae) for which the different forms or "phases" may be so different in appearance and behaviour that they were at one time thought to be separate species (Uvarov, 1921).

Individual locusts living at low densities (phase *solitaria*) behave as typical grasshoppers, avoiding other individuals of the same species, while those living in crowded conditions (phase *gregaria*) are gregarious and occur in dense, migrating swarms (Key, 1950; Kennedy, 1956, 1961; Uvarov, 1966). Phase changes are complex and affect many characters, such as size, shape, colour, rate of development, behaviour and fecundity; but basically they reflect a change in the locusts' metabolism to favour greater mobility. Phase *gregaria* is migratory both in the nymphal and adult stages. Gregarious adults are smaller and relatively longer winged, and their metabolic rates are higher than those of *solitaria*; *gregaria* eat more and retain less for growth and storage. These changes appear to be possible only at the expense of fecundity, for female *gregaria* lay fewer eggs. This is compensated for to some extent by their eggs being bigger, and nymphs hatching from *gregaria* eggs are heavier and can survive longer when starved than those from *solitaria*. The rates of development of eggs and nymphs are also faster for *gregaria*. All of these changes make gregarious locusts better fitted for a migratory life in the uncertain environment away from their permanent habitats, and it seems likely that phase changes are adaptations to meet the hazards of emigration when population density is high.

It is possible that phase changes are the direct result of intra-specific competition for space. Certainly competition appears to be the cause of density-dependent emigration from their permanent habitats. On the other hand, many other Acrididae show density-dependent emigration without these complex changes occurring. These species do not have such scattered habitats as do locusts, and the factors which favour increases in their numbers tend to make surrounding areas more suitable for them (Dempster, 1963b). There is less need for them to be very mobile.

In practice there is probably little point in distinguishing between phase changes and the changes brought about by intra-specific competition, since the two are closely linked. Strictly speaking however, they are not an impairment resulting from the harmful effects of competition, but are an evolved adaptation which improves the chance of survival of emigrating individuals. They are directly comparable with the development of winged forms of such insects as aphids when larvae or viviparous adults are crowded. These changes are triggered off by increases in density, but there is little to suggest that competition for space is occurring.

II. Genetic Changes

A completely different type of change in the quality of individuals is described by Wellington (1957, 1960, 1964). He studied the population ecology of the western tent caterpillar (*Malacosoma pluviale*) in Canada, and showed big variations in the average vigour of larvae at different densities due to the survival of weaker genotypes during periods of population growth. This species lays its eggs in batches of 100–300 and the caterpillars are gregarious. Those from a batch of eggs stay together and construct a communal tent of silk in which they shelter and moult. They leave the tent to feed, but trail a silk thread behind them as they walk. Colonies of this species contained different types of larvae which ranged from being very active to sluggish, and the proportions of these types of individual differed between colonies. Very active individuals tended to walk in straight lines and were strongly attracted towards light, and they quickly found food if placed singly on a twig. At the other extreme, sluggish individuals moved little, tended to stay together and could only find food if they followed the silk thread left by an active individual. Activity was genetically controlled, since more active adults produced more active larvae. Sluggish individuals were more prone to attack by a parasitic fly and by virus and bacterial diseases (Iwao and Wellington, 1970).

Wellington showed that populations were generally started by active females laying eggs in a new area. Their offspring included both active and sluggish individuals, but as the population built up the more active individuals, tended to emigrate, while the sluggish ones stayed. As the density rose the proportion of sluggish individuals rose, until the colonies became so close together that food became short, or disease broke out. Elsewhere new colonies were starting and so the cycle started again. Wellington thought that local extinction was inevitable unless better quality individuals immigrated, but a favourable climate had to persist for at least four generations to allow the deteriorating stock to exterminate itself, otherwise the most sluggish individuals were eliminated by bad weather.

Wellington's findings serve as a reminder that individuals within a population differ in their ability to survive and reproduce under different environmental conditions. Also, since genetically different individuals leave different numbers of progeny in the next generation, the genetic composition of populations is continually changing.

Fluctuations in population size will themselves generate changes in the genetic variability within the population. If conditions favour population growth, natural selection will be relaxed. This will inevitably lead to greater variability, since forms will survive which would be destroyed in more rigorous conditions. Once conditions become harsher, diversity will again be reduced due to the elimination of weaker genotypes as numbers drop. It is during the period of increase that diversity is greatest; a high but constant population will be less variable. Similarly, variability will be least during periods of population fall.

This variation in the average vigour of individuals during population fluctuations has led Chitty (1960, 1965) to suggest that genetic change could lead to greater population stability. His argument is that since population increase will result in the survival of many weaker genotypes, any harmful environmental factor will have a proportionally bigger effect at population peaks than at troughs. Wellington claims that his findings support this view of Chitty's.

It is very difficult to assess how important genetic effects of this sort are in wild populations. The impact of genetic variability on population size cannot be quantified, since it is impossible to determine the total genetic make up of individuals. Personally, I believe that it is unlikely that genetic variations contribute much to population stability. If it were so, one would expect mortality to be strongly density-dependent in rapidly fluctuating populations and there is little evidence of this from field studies. On the other hand, too little is known about the impact of genetic changes to be dogmatic about this.

6. Natural Enemies

All animal species are fed upon by natural enemies of one sort or another; either predators, parasites, or disease organisms. In some cases, these can play an important role in the natural control of their prey. Examples of this can be seen among the successful attempts at biological control of pests and in the effects that the elimination of predators, or disease, can have on animal numbers.

One of the best examples of biological control is that of the cottony-cushion scale (*Icerya purchasi*) on citrus in California. This pest is a native of Australia and it was introduced accidentally into California on young citrus trees. It flourished in its new environment to such an extent that it became a serious threat to the Citrus Industry. In Australia the scale was not abundant, apparently because of a number of native predators which fed on it. One of these, a ladybird beetle, *Rhodolia cardinalis*, was collected and released in California, and it quickly spread and reduced *Icerya* to very low numbers. It has since kept the pest below an economic level.

A parallel story can be found in the history of the rabbit (*Oryctolagus cuniculus*) in Britain (Sheail, 1971). Rabbits were introduced into Britain by the Normans, soon after the Conquest, and were initially kept in rabbit warrens for meat and fur. Every so often some escaped and slowly the rabbit spread over the country. It remained rare over much of the country however, until the eighteenth century, when farmers started growing more fodder crops during the winter, and fewer rabbits died from starvation. It then increased enormously in numbers, until it became probably the most important single pest in agriculture. In 1950 it was estimated that there were about 100,000,000 rabbits in Britain. In 1953–4 myxomatosis spread from France to Britain. The spread of this disease was undoubtedly aided by farmers releasing infected rabbits, but the effect was surprisingly dramatic. The numbers of the rabbit crashed and they have remained low ever since.

These are cases in which a natural enemy has been introduced to control the population size of an animal. The reverse can also occur, when Man eliminates the enemy of a animal and allow its numbers to increase enormously. This can be seen with the resurgence of pests after chemical control, due to the elimination of their natural enemies. Examples of this are described on pages 133 to 136 for *Pieris rapae* and *Panonychus ulmi*.

In spite of these examples of the impact that natural enemies can have, their precise effect is often extremely difficult to assess. As will be seen below, the mortality which they inflict on their prey is often determined by a complex of environmental factors, and few generalizations as to their effects can be made from existing data. This is one field of study which urgently demands more research, since so many applied problems in population ecology, require a knowledge of how natural enemies operate (see Chapter 11).

I. Disease

Infectious diseases can cause very high mortalities during epizootics (epidemics). Pathogens are transmitted by either ingesting contaminated food, by vectors, or by direct contact, so that the ease and speed of spread will depend partly upon population density. It will however, also depend upon other environmental factors which affect the survival of the organism during transmission. For example, many disease organisms are very dependent upon the right weather conditions for survival outside the bodies of their hosts.

The number of animals dying from a disease is not only dependent upon rates of transmission, it also depends upon the virulence of the pathogen and upon the resistance of the hosts. Overcrowding may lower the vigour of some animals, so that they become more susceptible to disease at high densities. There is then a tendency for epizootics to be associated with periods of high density, but stress due to other unfavourable environmental conditions may also trigger them off. Their association with high population densities is therefore imprecise and their occurrence tends to be sporadic.

The interaction of factors which determine the mortality caused by disease can be seen from Wellington's study of the western tent caterpillar, *Malacosoma pluviale* (Wellington, 1962). This species is attacked by a nuclear polyhedrosis virus which is transmitted from the female

moth through her eggs to the caterpillars. It is also spread by caterpillars eating foliage which has been contaminated by faeces and dead
bodies of infected individuals. The virus may remain as a latent infection,
not killing the caterpillar, unless the latter is stressed by unfavourable
conditions. Colonies of this moth contain individuals which range from
being sluggish to extremely active (see p. 39). When densities are high,
sluggish colonies are more affected by the virus than active ones, since
the individuals tend to stay together, and the disease spreads rapidly
among them. Wellington found that at the peak in population density
the appearance of symptoms of the disease was preceded by a period of
starvation imposed by cool, wet weather. This period of stress appeared
to activate the latent virus and disease spread rapidly through the population. Only active individuals survived the population crash which
followed, but many of these carried the virus in a latent form. As the
population increased again, the virus spread to both active and sluggish
individuals, but few died from the disease until the population was stressed
once more by bad weather.

The interdependence of stress and disease makes it very difficult to
determine the precise effect that pathogens have on the numbers of
their hosts. Frequently animals die from the combined effects of starvation, or some other stressing factor, and disease, so that the role of the
disease becomes uncertain. In the western tent caterpillar, inclement
weather caused both starvation and an outbreak of virus disease. There
are many other similar examples in the literature, both amongst invertebrates and vertebrates. For example, Jenkins *et al.* (1963) showed that
many red grouse (*Lagopus lagopus scoticus*) die in an emaciated condition
during spring and early summer. These birds frequently carry heavy
infections of tapeworms and nematodes (*Trichostrongylus*) (Table VII).
Grouse in both "good" and "poor" condition contained very high
numbers of *Trichostrongylus* in 1958 and 1959, but only those in "poor"
condition died. The majority of deaths were of non-breeding birds,

Table VII. Incidence of gut parasites in red grouse

	1956–7	1958	1959	1960	1961
% with tape worms	50	67	76	31	33
% with > 1000 *Trichostrongylus*	47	85	89	15	22
Mean No. *Trichostrongylus* in:—					
Grouse in good condition	245	1341	4168	—	—
Grouse in poor condition	2261	4102	7498	—	—

living in sub-optimum habitats, and there is little doubt that starvation was at least a predisposing cause of death.

The overall effects of disease are obviously complicated. Epizootics do tend to be density-dependent, but many pathogens occur at a low incidence which is quite independent of the density of their hosts. Far more quantitative work on the effects of pathogens is required, however, before their precise role can be assessed adequately.

II. Predators and Insect Parasites

Predators and insect parasites have such similar effects upon their prey populations that they can be considered together. Both are usually of a similar size to their prey, and both kill their prey, either before, or as a result of, their feeding. Parasitic insects are not true parasites but are parasitoids, since their adults are free-living and they invariably kill their hosts on completion of feeding. The female usually lays her eggs on, or into, the body of the prey and the larvae then feed on the prey and ultimately kill it. They differ from predators mainly in that one individual prey is sufficient for their full development.

The number of prey taken by predators depends upon a large number of environmental factors. Most prey species have evolved defence mechanisms which may give protection to some individuals. These include such devices as protective spines, distastefullness, predator avoidance and escape techniques, group protection, etc. Added to this, habitats frequently contain some sites which give prey more protection from predators. We saw an example of this in Chapter 3, when *Anthocoris sarothamni* experienced a relative shortage of prey (*Arytaina spartii*), due to the latter being hidden within the buds of its food plant, although it occurred at high densities. The number of a prey species taken also depends upon the number of alternative prey, since many predators are polyphagous. Weather also influences rates of predation, particularly in poikilothermic animals. Searching ability of predators and escape ability of prey are often markedly affected by weather. Lastly, and perhaps most importantly, the number of prey taken depends upon the densities of both prey and predator.

With so many environmental factors affecting predation, the response of predators to variations in the abundance of their prey is unlikely to be simple, and indeed, it has proved extremely difficult to study this in field. Most progress in the study of predation has been made by analysis of the individual components determining the predators' response to changes in the numbers of their prey. Solomon (1949), followed by Holling (1959), recognized two main responses of predators. First, a "functional response", each individual predator attacking more prey when the latter are at high densities. Secondly, he recognized a "numerical response" due to the numbers of a predator increasing with increasing prey density. Hassell (1966) took this idea further, and pointed out that the numerical response of predators can be immediate, because of aggregation, as well as delayed, because of better survival and reproduction of the predators, as a result of improved food supply. He therefore proposed a new terminology in which the predator's responses to prey density were divided into immediate, "behavioural responses", and delayed, "intergeneration responses". It is Hassell's terminology which is used here.

A. Behavioural Responses

The behavioural response of a predator may be divided into "individual" and "aggregate" components. The individual response results from changes in the behaviour of individual predators which lead to changes in their efficiency. For example, each individual predator may catch more prey when the latter are numerous than when they are sparse. The aggregate component occurs as a result of enemies concentrating on a particular prey when its numbers are high. Many polyphagous predators, for example, will switch their feeding habits to concentrate mainly on a particularly numerous prey species. Birds appear to develop a "searching image" for those prey species which are particularly abundant at the time (Tinbergen, 1960). Even very specific predators may be sufficiently mobile to concentrate on to areas where their prey are especially numerous. For example, many insect predators, such as ladybird beetles, only lay their eggs where their aphid prey are abundant. In this way they can ensure a plentiful supply of food for their offspring. As we shall see below, the behavioural response of a predator is potentially density-dependent, at least over a certain range of prey densities.

1. Individual Responses

Holling (1959) divided the individual behavioural response of predators (his functional response) into three basic types. First, the number of prey killed per predator can be directly proportional to prey density, when its pattern of searching is random and its rate of searching remains constant at all prey densities (Curve A in Fig. 11). De Bach and Smith (1941) reported this type of response from the parasitic fly, *Musidifurax raptor* attacking pupae of *Musca domestica*. As Holling (1959) points out, however, too few pupae were used in this experiment to be certain that the response curve did not flatten out at higher densities.

The second type of response curve is that obtained in laboratory experiments for a number of insect parasites (Burnett, 1951, 1958; Ullyett, 1949a, b). In these, the number of prey attacked increased rapidly with initial increases in prey density. The curve flattened out at higher prey densities however, when the parasite had laid all of its eggs (Curve B, Fig. 11). An example of this type of response is seen in Burnett's

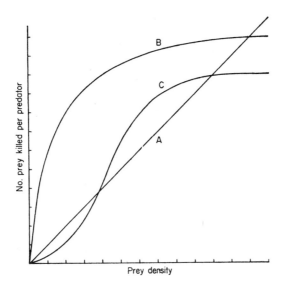

Fig. 11: The three basic types of individual behavioural response of predators to changes in prey numbers.

data for *Dahlbominus fuliginosus* attacking cocoons of *Neodiprion sertifer* (Burnett, 1951) (Fig. 12).

The last type of response recognized by Holling is a sigmoid curve (Curve C, Fig. 11). This type of curve has been demonstrated for small mammal predators (Fig. 13) by Holling (1959) and for an insect parasite by Embree (1966). In these, there is an initial increase in the rate of searching as prey density increases, but this falls off once more above a certain density as the predator becomes satiated.

Some predators, particularly vertebrate species, have been recorded killing prey far in excess of their food requirements. The evidence for this is largely anecdotal and may be misleading since many species create food-caches which are consumed later. Those studies which have been made on the relationship between predatory activity and hunger, suggest that in the wild excessive killing is rare (Mueller, 1973) but more information is required on this subject.

The individual behavioural response of predators is measured in

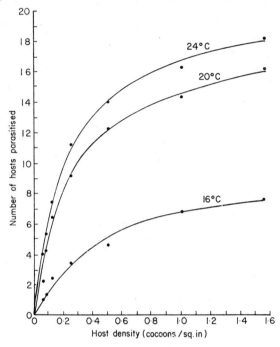

Fig. 12: The effect of host density on the number of *Neodiprion sertifer* attacked by *Dahlbominus fuliginosus* (Burnett, 1951).

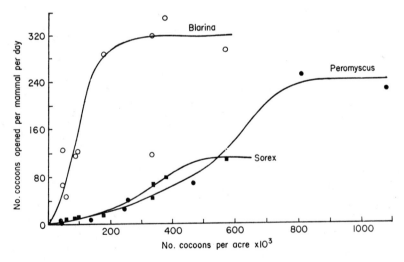

Fig. 13: The effect of host density on the number of *Neodiprion sertifer* cocoons taken by small mammals (Holling, 1959).

terms of the number of prey killed per individual predator. To understand the impact which this has upon the numbers of their prey, we
need to express numbers taken in terms of percentages of the prey population. Hassell (1966) discussed this and concluded that the individual
response curves can produce density-dependent mortality only under
certain circumstances. Obviously, Curve A (Fig. 11) results in a constant
percentage mortality at all densities. Curve B results in a decreasing
rate of mortality with increases in density (i.e. an inverse density-
dependent relationship). Curve C results in an initial density-dependent
mortality which reaches a peak and changes to an inverse density-
dependent mortality as the response curve flattens out. Hassell also
recognizes a fourth type of response curve, namely a type B curve
which does not pass through the origin. When this type of response is
converted to percentages of prey taken, the result is similar to that for
a sigmoid curve. Hassell's conclusions are summarized in Fig. 14.

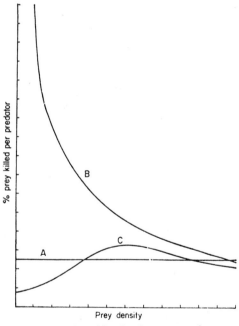

Fig. 14: Percentage mortality produced by the three types of response shown in Fig. 11.

2. Aggregate Responses

The aggregate behavioural response of predators to changes in their
prey's numbers is less easily studied experimentally. There have however, been many examples reported in the field of predators aggregating

onto areas of high prey density. Most of the evidence for immediate numerical responses of predators to high densities of prey are based on correlations between prey and predator numbers and these could be fortuitous. On the other hand, such differences in predator density can frequently be associated with their dispersion behaviour. For example, Chandler (1968) showed that many aphidophagous Syrphidae (hover-flies) only lay their eggs on plants on which are large numbers of aphids. The number of prey required for oviposition appears to be different for different species of syrphid. Vertebrate predators also tend to aggregate onto high prey populations. Many insectivorous birds flock onto locust swarms (Smith and Popov, 1953; Hudleston, 1958). Gibb (1958, 1966) showed that tits (*Parus* spp.) feeding on the larvae and pupae of the moth (*Ernarmonia conicolana*) in pine cones, concentrate onto areas where this prey is most abundant. There appears to be a threshold density, below which tits ignore *Ernarmonia*.

This aggregate behavioural response of predators may result in density-dependent mortality of the prey, provided the response is large enough. A subproportional response by the predator to changes in prey density will, however, result in density-independent or inversely density-dependent mortality.

B. Intergeneration Responses

An increase in prey density can result in an increased number of predators in the next generation, as a result of improved survival or reproduction of the predator. This effect is always delayed so that the response cannot be directly density-dependent, unless the predator has a far

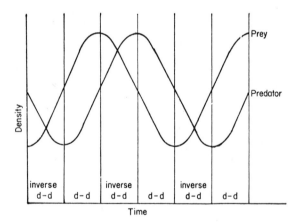

Fig. 15: The density relationships produced by an intergeneration response in predator numbers.

shorter generation-time than its prey, which would be unusual. More commonly it will result in a delayed density-dependent response by the predator (see p. 11).

The precise effect that this delayed density-dependent response has on the prey's population will depend upon the extent of the lag between the two populations (Fig. 15). For part of the cycle the response will be density-dependent, but for the other part it will be inversely density-dependent. As with the behavioural response of predators, this response is in terms of number of prey consumed, so that even the density-dependent part of the cycle may not lead to density-dependent mortality. This will depend upon the predator's numbers increasing sufficiently fast to produce a proportional increase in mortality.

C. The Overall Effect

It is extremely unlikely that any hard and fast rule can be made about the effect that natural enemies can have upon populations of their prey. The overall effect of a predator, or insect parasite, will be the combined effect of its behavioural and intergeneration responses. As we have seen,

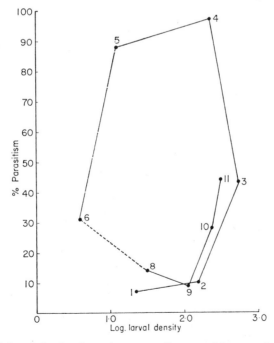

Fig. 16: The delayed density-dependent mortality caused by parasites of the black-headed budworm (Morris, 1959).

the mortality resulting from these responses may or may not be related to density.

Examples can be found from field studies of predation which show every possible type of density related mortality. In some cases, the inter-generation responses of the predator outweighs other responses, so that percentage mortality is delayed density-dependent. Examples of this are seen in Figs. 16 and 17, which show total parasitism of the black-

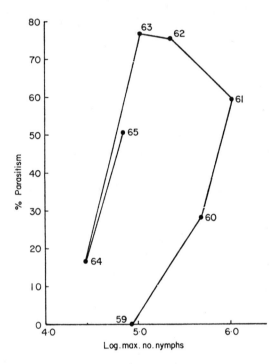

Fig. 17: The delayed density-dependent parasitism of *Leiophron* on *Asciodema* (Waloff, 1967).

headed budworm, *Acleris variana* (Morris, 1959), and the rates of parasitism of *Asciodema obsoletum* by *Leiophron heterocordyli* (Waloff, 1967). In both cases, one obtains an anti-clockwise plot, when joining points for successive generations which indicates a delayed density dependence (see p. 18). Other studies have shown an overall density dependence in the mortality caused by predators. Hassell (1966) gives an example of this when quoting Varley and Gradwell's (1963) work on winter moth (*Operophtera brumata*). Pupal mortality in this moth is thought to be due mainly to predators, but several species are involved. There

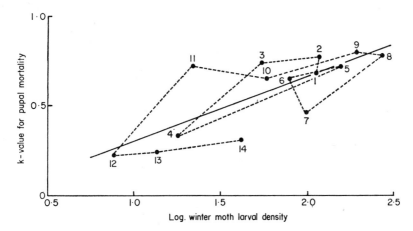

Fig. 18: Density-dependent mortality caused by predators on the pupae of winter moth (Varley and Gradwell, 1963; Hassell, 1966).

appears to be an overall density dependence in this mortality (Fig. 18) which may be due to a behavioural response by some, or all, of the predators, but the scatter of points around the line suggests that there is also an important intergeneration response present. Inverse density-dependent relationships have also been found; for example, in the rate of parasitism of the eggs of the gypsy moth (Bess, 1961) and in the predation by anthocorids on the sycamore aphid, *Drepanosiphon platanoides* (Dixon and Russel, 1972). Lastly, for very many species, mortality from natural enemies appears to be density-independent.

There is now clear evidence to show that the vast majority of predators do not act as density-dependent factors in the way suggested by Nicholson (1933) (see Chapter 10). On the other hand, it is possible to visualize the situation in which the aggregate behavioural response of predators results in a density-dependent mortality over a fairly wide range of prey densities. Far more quantitative studies of field populations are required to generalize.

One last point requires stressing. The proof that a mortality factor is density-dependent does not necessarily indicate that it plays an important role in natural control. This will depend upon the strength of its action and upon its timing in relation to other mortalities. As an example, Dempster (1968a) showed that predation on *Arytaina spartii* by *Anthocoris sarothamni* and *A. nemoralis* was density-dependent, but they were incapable of controlling the numbers of *Arytaina* owing to the large and variable, contemporaneous mortality caused by other predators.

7. Weather

For all species there is a limited range of physical conditions within which they can survive and reproduce. Conditions outside this range will either kill them, or prevent their reproduction. Extremes in unfavourable weather can then have drastic effects upon the size of animal populations.

Besides these harmful effects of extremes in conditions, virtually all an animal's activities are dependent upon the weather, so that rates of growth, maturation, movement and dispersal, feeding, mating, egg-laying, etc., are all affected (see Uvarov, 1931; Andrewartha and Birch, 1954). This is particularly true for poikilothermic species, since their rates of metabolism are totally dependent upon external physical conditions, but warm blooded species are also not immune from such effects.

Added to this, the food supply of most animals is dependent upon the weather, either through rates of plant growth, or through changes in the populations of prey animals. The supply of other resources, such as drinking water, shelter provided by vegetation, hibernating sites and egg-laying sites, may also depend upon the weather; so that climatic variations can greatly alter the carrying capacity of some habitats.

All of these effects mean that weather factors can have an enormous impact on populations of some animals; so much so, that they frequently act as the "key factor" determining population trends (see p. 15). Before looking at the overall influence of weather however, let us first look at the detailed effects that it can have on survival and reproduction.

I. Effects on Survival

Excessively high or low temperatures, drought or excessive moisture can all be lethal to animals. The distribution of species in time and space is frequently determined by limiting environmental factors of this sort. Most species live and attempt to reproduce only in predominantly favourable conditions. Thus the life cycles of many species are synchronized with the seasons, and long periods of unfavourable weather are often avoided either by entering a diapause or dormancy, or by migrating to a more favourable area. In spite of this safeguard, very high death-rates can occur as a result of inclement weather. In Britain,

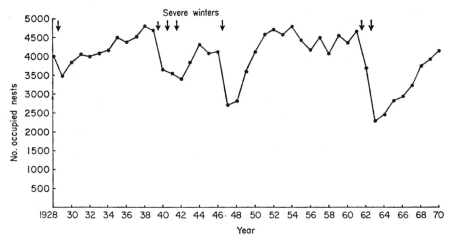

Fig. 19: The number of nests occupied by herons in England and Wales 1928–1970 (Stafford, 1971).

severe winters, in which there is continuous frost and snow for several months, kill large numbers of animals. Elton (1927) lists a number of such winters dating back to the twelfth century, when high death-rates have been recorded amongst small birds, such as blackbirds, thrushes and tits. In these, winter deaths are probably due to starvation rather than to lethal temperatures. The impact that winter mortality of this sort can have on a species can be seen in Fig. 19, which shows the number of nests occupied by herons (*Ardea cinerea*) in England and Wales each year since 1928 (Stafford, 1971). The breeding population of this bird normally fluctuates around 4,000–4,500, but declines markedly after hard winters. This is a fish-eating bird and it is unable to find sufficient food when inland waters become frozen for long periods.

Local populations can be completely eliminated by abnormal weather. Ehrlich *et al.* (1972) record a population of the butterfly *Glaucopsyche lygdamus* being reduced to extinction by a freak snowstorm in late June, 1969, in Colorado, U.S.A. I have seen the same thing happen with a

c

population of the cinnabar moth (*Tyria jacobaeae*). A small population of this species in Monks Wood National Nature Reserve, England, was destroyed by flooding caused by abnormally heavy rainfall in the summer of 1968. Examples of this sort can also be found for vertebrates: Blair (1957) describes the extinction of populations of a lizard (*Anolis carolinensis*) and a frog (*Rana catesbeiana*) by a severe drought. Population extinction is, of course, far more likely to occur near the edge of the geographical, or ecological, range of an animal. Nearer the centre of its distribution there is less likelihood of conditions being so extremely unfavourable.

The direct harmful effects of weather on the survival of animals occur only with extreme conditions, that is those outside the range to which the species is adapted. Within the range of favourable conditions however, weather still has many indirect effects on survival, since virtually all causes of mortality may be affected in one way or another by the weather.

Variations in the weather can markedly affect the impact that natural enemies have on their prey. Disease organisms depend to a large extent upon the right conditions for spread, while the resistance of their hosts to infection and death is affected both directly, and indirectly through their food supply, by the weather. We saw an example of this on p. 43, with the effect of a virus disease on the western tent caterpillar. The action of parasites and predators, and the ability of prey species to avoid these enemies, are both affected by the weather. For example, the ability of tawny owls (*Strix aluco*) to catch their rodent prey is reduced during rainy weather, since this owl locates its prey mainly by hearing (Southern, 1970). On the other hand, predation on *Pieris rapae* by the ground-beetle, *Harpalus rufipes*, is greater during wet weather, since this beetle tends to be inactive during dry periods (Dempster, 1967). Synchronization between populations of prey and their enemies may also be upset by variations in weather; when their dates of emergence, or rates of development, are not affected to the same extent by changes in the physical conditions.

Inter- and intra-specific competition may also depend upon the weather. As we saw on p. 30, different species may have a competitive advantage over others under different environmental conditions. Added to this, competition depends upon the carrying capacity of the environment, and this may vary enormously in response to changes in the weather.

It can be seen then that even within the range of suitable conditions for survival, the weather can have enormous indirect effects on the numbers of animals dying.

II. Effects on Reproduction

Cold blooded animals are invariably dependent upon the right weather conditions for maximum reproduction. As with survival, reproduction may be directly impaired or enhanced by the weather, and also indirectly affected through food supply. In these species, recruitment to the population by egg-laying, or by the hatching of eggs often closely follows daily variations in the weather. Examples of this can be seen in Figs. 20 and 21

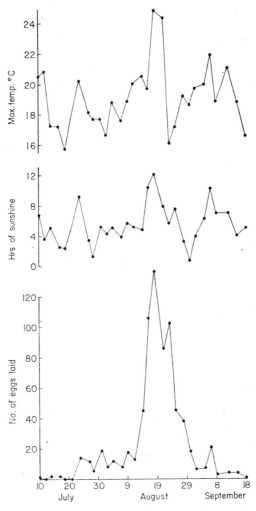

Fig. 20: The effects of temperature and insolation on the number of eggs laid by *Pieris rapae*.

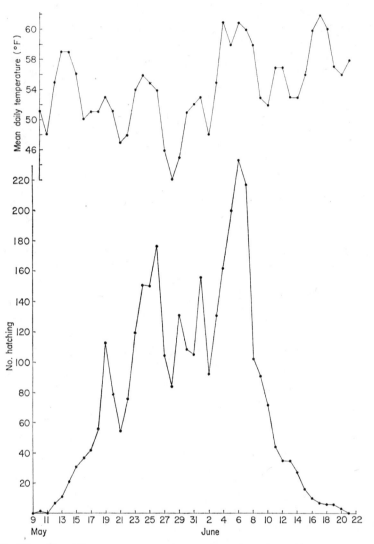

Fig. 21: The effect of temperature on the number of *Heterocordylus tibialis* hatching.

for two species of insect. Under constant conditions both of these curves would probably follow a normal or Gaussian distribution, i.e. a symmetrical bell-shaped curve, but this has been modified by climatic variations. Unfavourable weather at the time of reproduction may greatly reduce the size of a population, whilst population outbreaks may result from enhanced reproduction due to abnormally favourable conditions.

Warm blooded species are less dependent upon the immediate weather conditions, although cold weather and sparse animal food at the time of egg-laying may cause a small reduction in the normal clutch size in the blackbird (*Turdus merula*) and the swift (*Apus apus*) (Lack, 1966). More commonly, the timing of breeding and the size of the clutch of birds are dependent upon the weather conditions prior to breeding, when the birds are laying down the food reserves needed to form eggs. For example, the red grouse (*Lagopus lagopus scoticus*) lays a smaller clutch of eggs in years when heather, its principal food plant, has been damaged by low temperatures (Jenkins *et al.*, 1963). Similarly, great, tits (*Parus major*) start breeding earlier, and lay more eggs per female, in years when temperatures during early spring are high and insect food is abundant (Lack, 1966).

For all animals, reproduction is dependent upon an adequate food supply and this is invariably affected by the weather. The supply of food for herbivores and scavengers is obviously dependent upon the right conditions for plant growth, while the food supply of predators is also determined ultimately by plant growth and its effects on the numbers of animals lower down the food chain.

III. Effects on Habitats

The carrying capacity of a habitat is not constant, but is fluctuating continuously in response to environmental factors, of which the weather is one of the most important. We have already seen that the food supply of all animals is ultimately dependent upon plant growth, but other resources, such as shelter, hibernation sites and egg-laying sites, may also be affected by the type of plant cover in the habitat, and therefore by the weather. Added to this, drinking water is needed by many terrestrial species and the availability of this is frequently determined by rainfall.

Many habitats may be only temporarily suitable for some animals due to seasonal variations in the weather. Thus the flowers and fruits of many plants, and some fresh water habitats such as temporary pools, may also be available at certain times of the year. The survival of these, and other shorter-lived habitats, such as dung, carrion and fungi, may depend upon daily changes in the weather as well as seasonal ones. Thus the weather plays a large role in determining the availability of suitable, temporary habitats for some species, as well as altering the carrying capacity of more permanent habitats.

IV. Overall Effects

Variations in the weather have repercussions on virtually all aspects of the population ecology of most animals. Frequently, only the most obvious effects can be measured when they alter survival, reproduction, or the habitat, but almost all activity and behaviour is dependent upon the weather. Some aspects of the impact of weather, such as its effects on the proportion of a population dispersing, have scarcely been studied. Because of the over-riding impact that weather has, particularly in poikilothermic animals, correlations have been found between population outbreaks of many pest species and weather (see for example, Dempster, 1963b, for locusts). The reason behind these correlations are frequently very poorly understood however.

Perhaps the best way of demonstrating just how complex the effects of weather can be, is to look in detail at its impact on one species. A good example is the Moroccan locust (*Dociostaurus maroccanus*), since the numbers of this species are particularly sensitive to variations in weather.

In Cyprus the habitat of the Moroccan locust is characterized by a dry-steppe or semi-desert vegetation, consisting of annuals which grow rapidly during early spring, so that there is a short period of lush growth. By the end of spring, however, they have seeded and died. The life-cycle of the locust is timed to this changing habitat by an egg diapause which ensures that hatching does not take place until the first warm days of spring, when the hoppers find abundant green food. By the time the adults appear, however, the ephemeral vegetation is drying up and green food is scarce. Egg laying takes place in early summer and all adults die with the onset of the summer drought. The eggs remain dormant through summer, autumn and winter, and hatch in the following spring when conditions are once more favourable.

The eggs of *Dociostaurus* must absorb water at the end of katatrepsis for further development to occur. This they normally do in early spring, and if insufficient rain falls at this time, many eggs may die from desiccation. Table VIII presents data from a three-year study of *Dociostaurus* (Dempster, 1957) and shows that in the spring of 1955, when only 54·8 mm of rain fell in January and February, almost a third of the eggs died in

Table VIII. The percentage mortality of eggs of *Dociostaurus* brought about by
desiccation (Dempster, 1957)

	1954	1955	1956
%Eggs dried	3·0	28·6	6·6
Rain (mm) during January and February	112·9	54·8	122·9

this way. This mortality was to a large extent outweighed by the warm,
dry spring bringing about an early hatch of eggs, since this led to adults
occurring before the summer drought began. This had a considerable
effect on fecundity, since adults lived longer in that year, and green
food was still available during the first ovipositions (Table IX). Even

Table IX. Fecundity of *Dociostaurus* (Dempster, 1957; Merton, 1959)

	1953	1954	1955	Cages
Dates of first adult	27 April	22 April	5 April	—
No egg pods/ ♀ ♀	0·3	0·4	0·9	3·2
No. egg/pod	28·1	27·6	30·0	31·2

so, fecundity in 1955 was considerably lower than Merton (1959)
obtained from caged locusts which were provided with green food
throughout their lives. Weather also directly affected survival of the
nymphs and adults; early nymphal mortality was particularly high in
1953 and 1955 due to cool, wet conditions.

The different stages in the life cycle of *Dociostaurus* have different
ecological requirements. Eggs are laid in firm, bare ground, but nymphs
and adults depend upon vegetation for food and shelter. Areas which
support large populations of the locust are characterized by having a
mosaic of bare ground and vegetation. Such a mosaic is usually unstable,
however, and the extent of its two components is greatly altered by rainfall. This sometimes leads to the crowding of one or other of the locust's
developmental stages and this can cause phase changes and gregarious
behaviour (see the section on Phase Changes on page 38). Probably
even more important in this respect is the instability of the vegetation.
With the death of the spring annuals, locusts tend to aggregate on the

surviving green vegetation, thus increasing their effective density. This led to the formation of hopper bands and to mass emigration of nymphs and adults in 1953.

The delicate timing of the locust's life cycle to a changing habitat makes it particularly sensitive to weather variations. Added to this, its developmental stages have different and conflicting weather requirements. Moisture is needed for egg development and for the green food which is required by the active stages for good survival and fecundity; but wet weather is detrimental to both nymphs and adults, which need warm, dry, sunny conditions for optimum survival. Also weather plays an important role in determining the extent to which the locust is crowded and so undergoes phase changes which affect both dispersal and fecundity. As can be seen, the overall effects of weather variations can be extremely complex.

In view of the complexity in the effects of the weather, it would perhaps be surprising if its action fell neatly into any classification of density relationships. However, since population size cannot affect the severity of the effect of the weather, its action is probably invariably density-independent. On the other hand, if there is a limited supply of shelters from unfavourable conditions, a higher proportion of a population may be affected by the weather when population density is high. In this case it is arguable that the effect of the weather is density-dependent. Personally, I prefer the view that this density-dependent effect is the result of intra-specific competition for shelter, in the same way as for any other resource. Admittedly, shelter only becomes a requirement at times of unfavourable weather, but then many other resources are only required at certain times. The argument is perhaps an academic one since the effect is still density-dependent, no matter how you choose to describe the event.

8. Detailed Population Studies

Population studies aim at answering three basic questions about an animal. First, what causes the fluctuations in its numbers from one year to another? Secondly, what determines the extent of these fluctuations? Thirdly, what limits the distribution of the species? As we saw in Chapter 2, the first two of these questions can best be answered by an intensive study of a population over a long period of time. Ideally, a series of age-specific life tables can then be constructed and analyzed to determine the impact of the various environmental factors that have been measured. The third question requires a different approach, since here we are interested in comparisons between populations in different localities. In no single species have all three questions been answered adequately. However, there is a growing number of long-term studies which go some way towards answering the first two questions. In this chapter we shall be looking at some of these.

The criterion which I have used in choosing the examples to be included here is that there should be at least five year's data published in a form which makes it possible to construct age-specific life tables which can be analyzed by the k-factor technique (see Chapter 2). This limits the choice of possible species to a few insects and birds. It has the advantage however, that data for each species can be compared directly.

I. The Cinnabar Moth

The cinnabar moth (*Tyria jacobaeae*) has a single generation each year. In Britain, the adult moths emerge in May from pupae which have

Table X. Life Tables for Cinnabar Moth 1966–1973 (Number per 150 m²)

Age Class	Cause of Change in Numbers	No. entering stage	1966		
			No. dying	% dying	% initial number accum'd
Adult					
	Sex ratio (% female)				
	Fecundity (eggs per female)				
Egg		2,120			
	Infertility		42	2·0	
	Failure to hatch		28	1·3	
	Miscellaneous		189	8·9	
				12·2	12·2
Larva I + II		1,861			
	Starvation		0	0·0	
	Arthropod predators + unknown		932	50·1	
				50·1	56·2
Larva III + IV		929			
	Starvation		0	0·0	
	Arthropod predators + unknown		198	21·3	
				21·3	65·6
Larva V		731			
	Apanteles		169	23·1	
	Starvation + failure at pupation		26	3·6	
				26·7	74·7
Pupa		536			
	Vertebrate predators		}427	79·7	
	Failure at emergence + unknown				
				79·7	94·9
Adult		109			

1967				1968				1969			
No. entering stage	No. dying	% dying	% initial number accum'd	No. entering stage	No. dying	% dying	% initial number accum'd	No. entering stage	No. dying	% dying	% initial number accum'd
109				362				1·5			
55·0				49·5				56·5			
285·2				92·1				73·2			
17,110				16,493				62			
	189	1·1			722	4·4			0	0·8	
	161	0·9			361	2·2			0	0·4	
	516	3·1			1,086	6·5			0	0·0	
		5·1	5·1			13·1	13·1			1·2	1·2
16,244				14,324				62			
	772	4·7			3,608	25·2			0	0·0	
	9,849	60·6			6,462	45·1			20	32·2	
		65·3	67·2			70·3	74·2			32·2	32·3
5,623				4,254				42			
	1,680	29·8			1,934	45·5			0	0·0	
	504	9·0			380	8·9			0	0·0	
		38·8	80·0			54·4	88·2			0·0	32·3
3,439				1,940				42			
	519	15·1			248	12·8			15	35·7	
	1,174	34·1			1,615	83·2			1	1·8	
		49·2	89·9			96·0	99·6			37·5	58·1
1,746				77				26			
	1,380	79·9			74	96·1			14	53·8	
	4	0·2			1·5	1·9			0	0·0	
		80·1	97·9			98·0	99·99			53·8	80·6
362				1·5				12			

Table X. *continued*

| Age Class | Cause of Change in Numbers | No. entering stage | 1970 | | % initial number accum'd |
			No. dying	% dying	
Adult		23			
	Sex ratio (% female)	47·4			
	Fecundity (eggs per female)	295·0			
Egg		3,197			
	Infertility		52	1·6	
	Failure to hatch		93	2·9	
	Miscellaneous		223	7·0	
				11·5	11·5
Larva I & II		2,829			
	Starvation		0	0·0	
	Arthropod predators + unknown		657	23·2	
				23·2	32·1
Larva III & IV		2,172			
	Starvation		0	0·0	
	Anthropod predators + unknown		151	7·0	
				7·0	36·8
Larva V		2,021			
	Apanteles		475	23·5	
	Starvation + failure at pupation		109	5·4	
				28·9	55·1
Pupa		1,437			
	Vertebrate predators		}1,137	79·1	
	Failure at emergence + unknown				
				79·1	90·6
Adult		300			

No. entering stage	No. dying	% dying	% initial number accum'd	No. entering stage	No. dying	% dying	% initial number accum'd	No. entering stage	No. dying	% dying	% initial number accum'd
		1971				1972				1973	
300				42				33			
55·7				50·0				51·1			
129·9				80·4				281·7			
21,699				1,689				4,749			
	277	1·3			45	2·7			43	0·9	
	263	1·2			7	0·4			21	0·4	
	1,041	4·8			95	5·6			94	2·0	
		7·3	7·3			8·7	8·7			3·3	3·3
20,118				1,542				4,591			
	2,416	12·0			0	0·0			74	1·6	
	11,173	55·5			1,293	83·8			1,895	41·3	
		67·5	69·9			83·8	85·3			42·9	44·8
6,529				249				2,622			
	3,432	52·6			0	0·0			1,500	57·2	
	2,219	34·0			80	32·1			584	22·3	
		86·6	96·0			32·1	90·0			79·5	88·7
878				169				538			
	46	5·2			13	7·9			30	5·5	
	417	47·5			3	1·7			175	32·5	
		52·7	98·1			9·6	90·9			38·0	93·0
415				153				333			
	361	87·0			}120	78·4			}171	51·4	
	12	2·9									
		89·9	99·8			78·4	98·0			51·4	96·6
42				33				162			

overwintered and they lay their eggs in batches of up to 150 on the under-
side of the basal leaves of ragwort (*Senecio jacobaea*). The eggs hatch in
2–3 weeks and the young caterpillars stay together on the leaf on which
they hatched until their first moult. They then develop their characteristic black and orange banding and they move to the top of the plants
where they feed upon the developing flowers. There are five larval
stages and when fully grown the caterpillars leave the plants, in July or
August, and pupate in the surface layers of the soil, often under a small
stone or amongst the roots of vegetation.

Since 1966 the numbers of each stage in the life cycle of this moth
have been counted on 47 ac (19 ha) of heathland at Weeting, Norfolk
(Dempster, 1971). The results from these counts are presented as a series
of life-tables in Table X. All of these data refer to the estimated number
in 150 m². It will be seen that the numbers of this moth have fluctuated
violently during the course of this study, from a minimum of 1·5 adults
to a maximum of 362. Egg numbers have varied to an even greater extent
from 62 in 1969 to 21,699 in 1971.

The factors causing mortality at various stages in the life cycle can
best be seen by looking at one year's data. In 1966, 2120 eggs were laid.
Egg mortality was only about 12% and it is estimated that 1861 larvae
hatched. By far the biggest cause of death of the eggs was the destruction
by rabbits of plants on which they occurred. Immediately after hatching
the death-rate was high; in 1966 about 56% of the caterpillars died
in the first two instars. This was mainly due to predation by arthropods.
Nine species of predator were identified as feeding on cinnabar caterpillars, of which by far the most important was a mite, *Erythraeus phal-
angoides*. As the caterpillars got bigger they became immune from attack
by these predators, but there was another peak in mortality in the fifth
instar, when the braconid parasite, *Apanteles popularis*, killed its hosts.
This killed 23% of the fifth stage caterpillars in 1966. There was a final
period of high mortality at or immediately after pupation, due probably
to vertebrate predators, particularly the mole, *Talpa europaea*. Close to
80% of the pupae were destroyed in this way in 1966.

In some years (1967, 1968, 1971, 1973) this pattern of mortality was
modified by starvation. In these years, the number of caterpillars was
so high that they completely defoliated their food plants and many died
of starvation. In the extreme case of 1968, close to 50% of the caterpillars
starved and only just over 1 adult/150 m² was obtained from more than
16,000 eggs.

Food shortage also had a marked effect on adult size and fecundity.
The estimated mean number of eggs per female was between 250–300
in those years when starvation did not occur, but was under 100 in

1968, 1969 and 1972, that is, those years following starvation. Many adults emigrated in 1968 and 1971, when their numbers were particularly high, and there was some immigration in 1970.

Ragwort is normally a biennial which passes the first year as a rosette, flowers in its second season and then dies. If damaged and prevented from flowering, however, it can behave as a perennial by repeated regeneration.

The soil at Weeting is poor and the vegetation is heavily overgrazed by rabbits. Under these conditions ragwort responds to defoliation by regeneration from rootbuds. This type of regeneration is particularly vigorous when young rosette plants are damaged. In the very wet summer of 1968, defoliation stimulated a considerable multiplication of ragwort as a result of regeneration, so that the number of plants rose

Table XI. The number of ragwort plants per m² and the weight of ragwort per larva at the time of hatching

	1966	1967	1968	1969	1970	1971	1972	1973
No. Rosette Plants	5·3	4·0	5·5	59·7	33·9	18·1	17·8	19·2
No. Flowering Plants	4·4	4·1	0·1	8·4	18·4	7·7	0·3	3·1
Total No. Plants	9·7	8·1	5·6	68·1	52·3	25·8	18·1	22·3
Wt. (g)/larva	1·36	0·14	0·04	162·07	90·37	0·25	0·91	0·78
Complete Defoliation		↑	↑			↑		↑
Rainfall (mm) (July–Sept)	164	127	296	129	113	153	182	

from 5·6 to 68·1/m² (Table XI). The other years when defoliation occurred were far drier and in these there was a slight reduction in the number of plants.

Variations in the total number of plants and in the proportion of them which were of flowering size, greatly altered the amount of food available to the caterpillars of the moth in different years (Table XI). This varied from 0·04 g/larva in 1968 to 162·07 g/larva in the following year. The plants are of course growing during the summer so that the total amount of food will change during the time when the caterpillars are present. On the other hand, about 1 g/larva appears to be needed at the time of hatching to prevent starvation occurring.

When a k-factor analysis (see p. 15 for details) is carried out on the data in Table X the following result is obtained (Fig. 22). Pupal mortality (k_5) and fifth-instar larval mortality (k_4) contribute most to total K and are therefore acting as key factors in determining trends from one year to the next. Total K is correlated with k_4 ($r = 0{\cdot}8343$) and with k_5 ($r = 0{\cdot}9004$). By dividing the larval stages into separate instars in

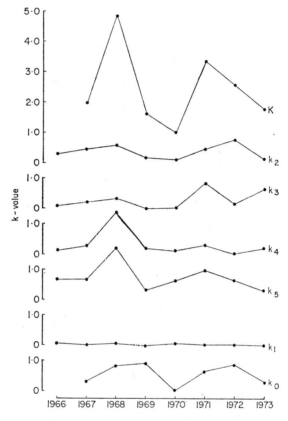

Fig. 22: A k-factor analysis of the cinnabar moth data in Table X. k_0 = Failure to reach maximum fecundity; k_1 = Egg mortality; k_2 = Early larval mortality; k_3 = Mid-larval mortality; k_4 = Late larval mortality; k_5 = Pupal mortality.

this way the effect of any mortality factor which acts on more than one instar may be hidden. Starvation has a marked effect on larval mortality in some years, but its timing varies between years. For example, it caused the high mortalities during instars III and IV in 1971 and during instar V in 1968.

One can obtain a better idea of the impact of larval mortalities by separating the different factors which are operating as individual k-values (Fig. 23). To enable this to be done, arthropod predation, starvation and parasitism from *Apanteles* are taken as operating in succession during larval life. This is not strictly true, since although starvation affects mainly older instars, it can cause high death-rates among very young larvae. However, this approach clearly shows that starvation acts as the key factor determining total larval mortality and this is correlated with total K $(r = 0.9490)$.

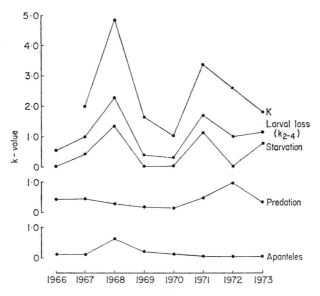

Fig. 23: The impact of k-factors for starvation, predation and parasitism, on larval mortality in the cinnabar moth.

Because of the impact of starvation, larval mortality (k_{2-4}) is positively correlated with larval density $(r = 0.8288, P < 0.02;$ Fig. 24). The two-way regression test (see p. 19 for details) does not prove density dependence however. This test assumes that the relationship with density is linear and this is clearly not so in this case. Intra-specific competition for food occurs only above a density of about 1,000 larvae/kg ragwort and so the relationship between k_{2-4} and density tends to be exponential. We shall find repeatedly during this chapter that the two-way regression test does not prove density dependence in cases of intra-specific competition because of this.

Both arthropod predation and parasitism by *Apanteles* are acting as density-independent factors. The inverse density-dependent relationship for *Apanteles* reported by Dempster (1971) has not been maintained in subsequent years.

Reduction in natality (k_0) includes variations in fecundity, adult mortality and dispersal. This is correlated with the log. maximum number of eggs in the previous year ($r = 0.8689$, $P < 0.05$) and so is acting in a delayed density-dependent way (Fig. 25). The reason for this is that fecundity is dependent upon the size of the adults, which in turn is determined by larval density and the supply of food. There is a good

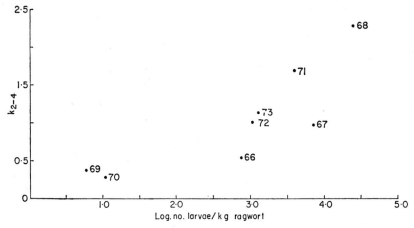

Fig. 24: The relationship between larval mortality (k_{2-4}) and larval density in the cinnabar moth.

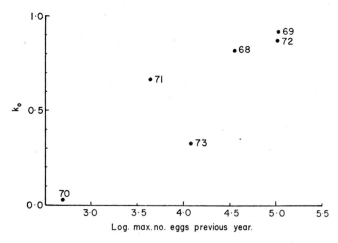

Fig. 25: Delayed density-dependent fecundity in the cinnabar moth.

correlation between pupal width and the number of eggs laid ($r = 0.7509, P < 0.001$; Dempster, 1971) and so mean pupal width can be used to estimate mean fecundity for each generation. When this is done, variations in fecundity can be seen to account for most of the variation in k_0 (Fig. 26). Mortality and dispersal were important only

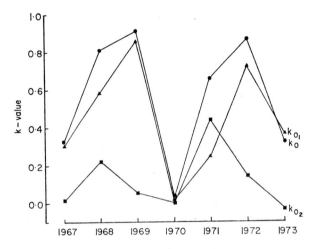

Fig. 26: The contributions of adult fecundity (k_{01}) and adult mortality and dispersal (k_{02}) to k_0 in the cinnabar moth.

in 1968 and 1971, the two years when adult numbers were highest. Increased adult density was shown to cause increased flight activity in the laboratory and this relationship results in ko_2 (mortality and dispersal) being dependent upon density, i.e. more adults emigrate when their numbers are high (Fig. 27). This tendency has little effect in limiting population size however, and does not prevent the moth reaching such high larval numbers that it eats out its food supply.

The peaks in this population of the cinnabar moth at Weeting are clearly limited by food supply. The crashes in numbers, brought about by starvation have led to a cycle in abundance of the moth and of its food plant. The rate of recovery of the moth population depends upon the rate of recovery of the ragwort. The plants made far better regrowth in the wet summer of 1968 than in other years of defoliation. In 1968, regeneration of the plants was also aided by the fact that defoliation had also occurred in the previous year (1967). This resulted in mainly rosette plants being present in 1968 (Table XI), and these regenerate far more readily from root buds than do larger plants.

The only factor which appeared to buffer the population against extinction at the times of food shortage was the heterogeneity which was present in the moth population and in the habitat. The earliest individuals were able to obtain sufficient food in the small areas where ragwort persisted longest, i.e. where ragwort density was high and caterpillar density was low. The large area covered by ragwort at Weeting (19 ha) also reduced the likelihood of extinction, since it supported a large enough population of the moth for it to survive the very high mortality at times of defoliation.

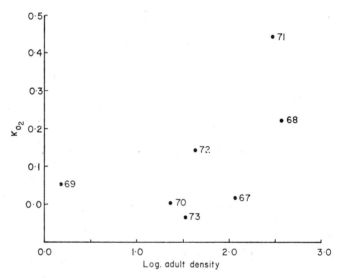

Fig. 27: The effect of density on adult mortality and dispersal (k_{02}) in the cinnabar moth.

Some populations of the cinnabar moth do not undergo such violent fluctuations and appear never to reach a size where they eat out their food supply. A population of this sort occurred at Monks Wood, Huntingdonshire. This site is on a heavy clay soil, rabbit grazing is minimal, and ragwort occurs only at a low density. The lusher vegetation supports a very large population of arthropod predators and these took a higher percentage of the young caterpillars than at Weeting. Pupal mortality was particularly high at Monks Wood, due probably to waterlogging of the soil. Cinnabar pupae can withstand considerable desiccation, but excessive moisture soon kills them. The data for the Monks Wood population were far less reliable than those from Weeting, but there was no evidence to suggest that pupal mortality was density-dependent. The population at Monks Wood became extinct as a result of heavy flooding during the autumn of 1968.

II. The Pine Looper

One of the longest series of age-specific life tables to have been published is for the pine looper, *Bupalus piniarius* (Klomp, 1965). This study was carried out on 6·8 ha of a pine plantation (*Pinus sylvestris*) in the National Park, "de Hoge Veluwe", in the Netherlands. The trees were 45 years old and 10 m high at the start of the study in 1950.

Pine looper moths emerge in May or June from pupae which have overwintered. Eggs are laid on the older pine needles in clusters of from 2–25, with up to 220 eggs being laid per female. After about 20 days the eggs hatch and the young caterpillars disperse by crawling. Five or six larval stages are passed through before the caterpillars are fully grown in mid-October. They then drop to the ground and pupate in the upper layers of the litter. There is a pupal diapause which prevents adults emerging until the following May.

Although Klomp's data record the changes in the moth's numbers from one stage in the life cycle to the next over a period of 14 years, they include little information on the causes of these changes. The only mortality factors which have been measured throughout the study are the insect parasites which attack the young stages of the moth. For this reason the complete life tables for this species have not been included here and readers are referred to Klomp (1965) for more details.

A large number of parasitic insects attack the young stages of *Bupalus*. Egg mortality is due mainly to the egg parasite *Trichogramma embryophagum* which killed between 7·5–69·2% of the eggs over the 14 years. This species is polyphagous and has five or six generations per year on a succession of different hosts. Its rate of attack on *Bupalus* is therefore unrelated to the latters density. Two parasites regularly attack the larval stages of *Bupalus*; a tachinid fly, *Strobliomyia fissicornis*, and a braconid wasp, *Apanteles caberae*. There were sporadic in their importance and showed no density dependence. Six species were recorded parasitizing the pupae, but again, none showed any density dependence in their rate of attack. A cytoplasmic polyhedral virus killed large numbers of caterpillars in 1955 and 1956, but in other years it was either absent or was at a very low incidence. A wide range of predators attack all stages of *Bupalus*, but no quantitative data have been obtained for these.

Table XII shows the numbers of *Bupalus* per m² entering each

Table XII. Life Table data from *Bulpalus piniarius*

		1950	1951	1952	1953	1954	1955	1956	1957	1958	1959	1960	1961	1962	1963	1964
Max potential natality No. ♀♀ × 220 eggs)		—	264	134	8·8	114	134	147	103	8·8	46	62	174	189	119	97
	k_0	—	0·2881	0·5589	0·1452	0·2716	0·6086	0·4039	0·6704	0·2121	0·2826	0·3452	0·4552	0·2809	0·4034	0·3636
Actual no. eggs		38	136	37	6·3	61	33	58	22	5·4	24	28	61	99	47	42
	k_1	0·1996	0·2304	0·3921	0·0833	0·3229	0·1663	0·1613	0·6612	0·0512	0·1601	0·1594	0·1832	0·1091	0·1950	0·3902
No. larvae I		24	80	15	5·2	29	22·5	40	4·8	4·8	16·6	19·4	40	77	30	17·1
	k_2	0·4025	0·5157	0·9720	0·0532	0·4017	0·2092	0·4231	0·4259	0·1249	0·4567	0·4127	0·1821	0·4920	0·2146	0·4201
No. larvae II–IV		9·5	24·4	1·6	4·6	11·5	13·9	15·1	1·8	3·6	5·8	7·5	26·3	24·8	18·3	6·5
	k_3	0·0432	0·0951	0·0902	0·0000	0·5166	0·6379	0·5662	0·3920	0·3010	0·4846	0·3188	0·6276	0·4702	0·3280	0·0688
No. larvae IV–VI		8·6	19·6	1·3	4·6	3·5	3·2	4·1	0·73	1·8	1·9	3·6	6·2	8·4	8·6	1·6
	k_4	0·1636	0·7482	0·3077	0·1857	0·0670	0·0737	0·3575	0·7494	0·2553	0·1996	0·1946	0·2483	0·1839	0·2443	
No. pupae		5·9	3·5	0·64	3·0	3·0	2·7	1·8	0·13	1·0	1·2	2·3	3·5	5·5	4·9	
	k_5	0·3395	0·4302	0·8062	0·4357	0·3310	0·2553	0·3011	0·1139	0·3188	0·3158	0·1856	0·2219	0·6990	0·7711	
No. adults		2·7	1·3	0·10	1·1	1·4	1·5	0·9	0·10	0·48	0·58	1·5	2·1	1·1	0·83	
	K	—	2·3077	3·1271	0·9031	1·9108	1·9510	2·2131	3·0128	1·2633	1·8994	1·6163	1·9183	2·2351	2·1564	

stage, and the values of the k-factor affecting each stage. These data differ slightly from those published by Klomp, since I have included variations in adult mortality, dispersal and fecundity in k_0, to make these results directly comparable with those for other species included in this chapter. Klomp dealt with these at the end of his analysis, as k_{10-12}.

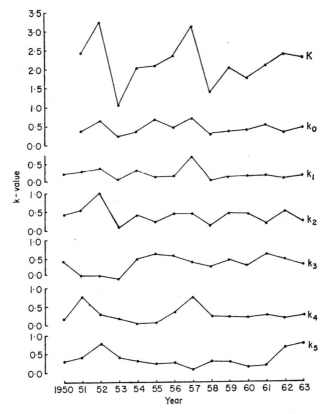

Fig. 28: A k-factor analysis of the pine looper data in Table XII. k_0 = Failure to reach maximum fecundity; k_1 = Egg mortality; k_2 = Early larval mortality; k_3 = Mid-larval mortality; k_4 = Late larval mortality; k_5 = Pupal mortality.

When individual k-factors are compared with total mortality, K, there is no obvious key factor operating on this population (Fig. 28). The highest correlation coefficients were obtained between K and k_0 (0·7394), k_1 (0·7700) and k_2 (0·7709). Total larval mortality (k_{2-4}) contributes considerably to total K, but then one would expect a closer correlation when individual age classes are lumped in this way, since total K is obtained by addition of the individual k-factors.

Larval density has a marked effect on the growth and fecundity of *Bupalus* (Gruys, 1970). Mutual interference between larvae occurs at very low densities and this results in smaller, less fecund adult moths. Klomp measured fecundity each year by keeping large numbers of moths individually in cages. Variations in fecundity between years (k_{0_1}) are given in Fig. 29, where it can be seen that, unlike the situation

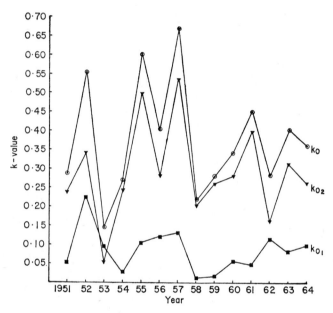

Fig. 29: The contributions of adult fecundity (k_{0_1}) and adult mortality and dispersal (k_{0_2}) to variations in k_0 in the pine looper.

found in the cinnabar moth (p. 73), these contribute little towards variations in k_0, compared with the effect of variations in adult mortality and dispersal (k_{0_2}). Because of the effect of larval density on adult size, fecundity acts as a delayed density-dependent factor, that is its action is dependent upon larval density in the previous generation ($r = 0.8335$, $P < 0.001$; Fig. 30).

There is some evidence to suggest that more moths tend to emigrate in years of high density (Gruys, 1970). k_0 does in fact show some correlation with the maximum initial number in each generation ($r = 0.523$, $0.10 > P > 0.05$), but the two-way test of final upon initial densities

(p. 19) fails to demonstrate density dependence since the slopes of both regressions are not significantly different from $b = 1$.

Although Klomp believes that there must be regulatory processes operating on this population of *Bupalus*, in my opinion his study has failed to identify them. None of the k-factors shows any strong density dependence, even though the data cover such a long series of years. This population of *Bupalus* fluctuated relatively little in size and it never reached a level where intra-specific competition for food occurred.

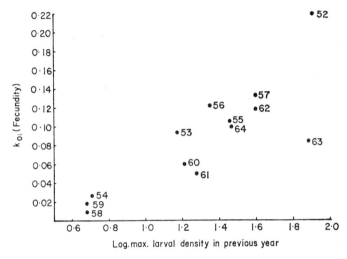

Fig. 30: Delayed density-dependent fecundity (k_{01}) in the pine looper.

In parts of eastern and central Europe however, this species is an important forest pest and it regularly defoliates pine, sometimes causing the death of many trees (Bevan, 1966). Varley (1949) presents data, obtained by Schwerdtfeger, for *Bupalus* numbers in an outbreak region at Letzlingen in Germany over a period of 60 years (Fig. 31). Pupal counts varied from $0.1-2500/100$ m^2, compared with $13-590/100$ m^2 in Klomp's population. At the peaks in the fluctuations at Letzlingen severe defoliation of the trees occurred over large areas. The effects of defoliation of pine are far more serious than for a deciduous tree, since each pine needle normally survives for 3 years before it drops. It therefore takes at least 3 years for a tree to replace its foliage after defoliation and this prolongs the period of food shortage for the moth. This appears to lead to a cycle of events which are very similar to those described for the cinnabar moth (p. 68), in which the population undergoes periodic crashes as a result of intra-specific competition for food. In Klomp's population of *Bulalus*, the environment is rarely sufficiently favourable to allow the population to build up to a level where intra-specific competition occurs. This appears to be due to the combined effect of a large array of factors, rather than to the density-dependent effect of one

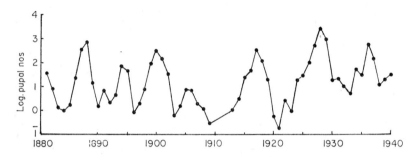

Fig. 31: Variations in the numbers of *Bupalus* in an outbreak region at Letzlingen, Germany (Varley, 1949).

factor. This is comparable to the Monks Wood population of cinnabar moth described on p. 74.

III. The Broom Beetle

The chrysomelid beetle, *Phytodecta olivacea*, is common on broom (*Sarothamnus scoparius*) in Southern England and was the subject of a population study by Richards and Waloff (1961).

This beetle has a single generation each year. Overwintering adults emerge in April from their hibernation sites in the litter under the broom bushes. They feed and oviposit on the foliage throughout the summer until the end of August, by which time they have either died or returned to hibernation until the following spring. There are four larval instars which feed on the broom, and the last one, when fully fed, enters the soil to pupate. The pupae give rise to adults from August to October and these feed on the broom before returning to the soil for hibernation. These adults are sexually immature and do not mate or oviposit until the following year. A varying proportion of adults survive and reproduce for a second season. Since egg-laying takes place over a period of about 3 months, all stages from egg to adult are found during most of the summer. The adult beetles have poor powers of dispersal, so that the population being studied was virtually self-contained.

Table XIII summarizes the results obtained by Richards and Waloff during their five year study of *Phytodecta* in a 2-ac (0·81 ha) area of broom at Ascot, Berkshire. It will be seen that there was a three-fold variation in the number of adults present at the beginning of the breeding season each year. Average fecundity varied from 32–82 eggs per female. This was far lower than the 250–300 eggs per female obtained in the laboratory (Waloff and Richards, 1958), but the latter do not include data from females which died from disease and parasites.

Each year there was a very heavy mortality (60–90%) of the eggs and young larvae, particularly during the early part of the summer. This was so high in some years that first stage larvae were not seen in the field until the end of June, 6 weeks after egg-laying began. Hatching normally occurs in about 2 weeks. The bulk of this mortality was due to the activities of a large number of predatory insects, especially Heteroptera (Miridae, Anthocoridae and Nabidae). This was confirmed quantitatively in 1957 and 1958, by the identification of the food of these predators by means of a serological technique (Dempster, 1960). All of these predators are polyphagous, feeding on many other species of prey besides *Phytodecta*. Egg infertility ranged from 4–10% and less than 1% of the eggs was destroyed by insect parasites. A small percentage of the larvae was also parasitized, by a number of insects, of which the fly, *Meigenia mutabilis*, was most important.

Mortality during the pupal stage was probably due mainly to predators (Dempster *et al.*, 1959). This ranged from 25–84% during the 5-year period. Soil living arthropods, such as Carabidae, were probably the most important predators at this time.

Adult beetles spend much of the year hibernating in the litter under the plants. Many of them are destroyed by a braconid parasite, *Perilitus dubius* and by fungal disease, *Beauveria bassiana*. There was reason for thinking that the mortality caused by *Beauveria* was under-estimated and Richards and Waloff believed that much of the winter mortality of adults was from this cause.

The effects of the predators of the early stages of *Phytodecta* was made greater by the concentration of the populations by the death of plants in some years. About half of the plants died during the winters of 1955–6 and 1957–8. Many had reached the end of their natural life (10–15 years) and had become susceptible to frost and were unable to survive a heavy production of seed. In the following springs, adults laid heavily on the surviving plants, so that the density of eggs was increased (see Table XIV). Alternative prey to the predators, such as aphids and psyllids were low in both years, and so mortality of the eggs and larvae of *Phytodecta* from predation was especially high (89% in 1956 and 81% in 1958).

Table XIII. Life Table data for *Phytodecta olivacea*

Age class	Cause of change in numbers	1954				1955			
		No.	No. dying	% dying	% Initial No. accum'd	No.	No. dying	% dying	% Initial No. accum'd
Adults		11,820				16,184			
	Sex ratio (% ♀♀)	47·4				56·5			
	Fecundity (eggs/♀♀)	82·1				72·1			
Eggs + larvae		460,169				659,554			
	Egg infertility		46,937	10·2			39,573	6·0	
	Egg + larval parasites		51,539	11·2			60,019	9·1	
	Arthropod predators + unknown causes		297,754	64·7			422,352	64·0	
				86·1	86·1			79·1	79·1
Pupae		63,939				137,610			
	Predation in soil + unknown causes		29,884	46·7			99,766	72·5	
				46·7	92·6			72·5	94·3
Adults (pre-winter)		34,055				37,844			
	Periletus		4,836	14·2			3,747	9·9	
	Beauveria		3,916	11·5			7,190	19·0	
	Removed to laboratory + unknown causes		11,787	34·6			14,860	39·3	
				60·3	97·1			68·2	98·2
Adults (post-winter)		13,516				12,047			
Surviving adults from previous year		2,668				4,980			

	1956				1957				1958		
No.	No. dying	% dying	% Initial No. accum'd	No.	No. dying	% dying	% Initial No. accum'd	No.	No. dying	% dying	% Initial No. accum'd
17,027				6,393				6,759			
50·0				58·3				56·5			
82·4				54·1				32·7			
701,563				201,760				125,039			
	25,256	3·6			9,866	4·9			10,003	8·0	
	41,392	5·9			7,263	3·6			3,238	2·6	
	627,775	89·5			139,805	69·3			101,344	81·0	
		99·0	99·0			77·8	77·8			91·6	91·6
7,140				44,826				10,454			
	1,843	25·8			37,482	83·6			5,098	48·8	
		25·8	99·2			83·6	96·4			48·8	95·7
5,297				7,344				5,356			
	1,398	26·4			1,292	17·6			268	5·0	
	122	2·3			0	0·0			193	3·6	
	938	17·7			1,177	16·0			2,153	40·2	
		46·4	99·6			33·6	97·6			48·8	97·8
2,839				4,875				2,742			
3,554				1,884				1,258			

Table XIV. Showing the concentration of the young stages of *Phytodecta* due to the death of broom plants

	1954	1955	1956	1957	1958
Area covered by broom (m²)	1764	1707	874	953	529
No. armfuls of broom	4769	4615	2103	2576	1429
No. eggs/armful	96·5	142·9	333·6	78·3	87·5

If a k-factor analysis is carried out on the data in Table XIII, the following results are obtained (Table XV, Fig. 32). Egg and larval mortality (k_1) contributes most to total generation mortality K (correlation coefficient $= 0.8605$). Pupal mortality (k_2) appears to be inversely related to k_1, but this relationship is not statistically significant. Reduced natality (k_0) increased markedly in 1957 and 1958, possibly due to a reduced nutritive state of the old broom plants affecting adult fecundity.

Table XV. A k-factor analysis of the data in Table XIII

	1954	1955	1956	1957	1958
Log. Max. Natality (No. ♀♀ × 250)	6·1463	6·3591	6·3279	5·9693	5·9798
k_0	0·4833	0·5398	0·4818	0·6645	0·8828
Log. No. Eggs + Larvae	5·6630	5·8193	5·8461	5·3048	5·0970
k_1	0·8572	0·6807	1·9924	0·6532	1·0777
Log. No. Pupae	4·8058	5·1386	3·8537	4·6516	4·0193
k_2	0·2736	0·5606	0·1296	0·7857	0·2904
Log. No. Adults (autumn)	4·5322	4·5780	3·7241	3·8659	3·7289
k_3	0·4014	0·4972	0·2709	0·1778	0·2908
Log. No. Adults (spring)	4·1308	4·0808	3·4532	3·6881	3·4381
K	2·0155	2·2783	2·8747	2·2812	2·5417

None of the k-factors is density-dependent. Adult, winter mortality (k_3) is weakly correlated with log. adult density $(r = 0.8556, d.f. = 3, P > 0.05)$. The two-way regression test of initial and final densities shows

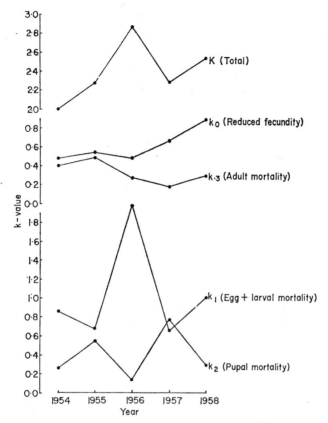

Fig 32: A *k*-factor analysis of the population data for *Phytodecta* in Table XV. k_0 = Failure to reach maximum fecundity; k_1 = Egg and larval mortality; k_2 = Pupal mortality; k_3 = Adult, winter mortality.

that k_3 is not density-dependent however. The action of *Beauveria* is correlated with adult density ($r = 0.9069$, $P < 0.05$) and the two-way regression test shows that it is density-dependent. Any stabilizing action of *Beauveria* on *Phytodecta* numbers is likely to be lost however, because of the disturbing action of other factors making up k_3, especially *Periletus*. It is possible that data for more years would prove k_3 to be density-dependent, but the slope of k_3 on log. adult density is only 0.2448, so that it is unlikely to have much stabilizing effect.

The numbers of the broom beetle are determined by a complex of factors, of which, egg and larval mortality, caused by a number of polyphagous predators, contributes most to variations between years. These were particularly important during the five years of this study because of the concentration of *Phytodecta* prey in 1956 and 1958, brought about by death of many of the broom bushes. None of the factors measured appears to be sufficiently density-dependent to compensate for these variations, but clearly 5 years is rather a short period in which to detect density dependence with any confidence.

IV. The Edible Cockle

Apart from insects and birds, the molluscs are probably the most thoroughly studied group of animals. These are relatively long-lived, and growth rings on their shells enable one to separate different age-classes. A big gap in the data for molluscan populations occurs however, in the very young stages, since these are difficult to study, especially when they are aquatic. This disadvantage applies to the data which are described below for the edible cockle (*Cardium edule*). I have chosen to include this species however, because it has such a different way of life to the other animals described in this chapter.

The cockle is a sedentary, inter-tidal, bivalve mollusc (Lamelli-branchiata), which burrows in sandy beaches, especially in river estuaries. In common with other bivalves it is a filter feeder, living on suspended detritus and microscopic organisms which are brought in by the tide. Growth is restricted to the summer months, and virtually stops between October and May. Although the largest one-year old individuals may produce a few eggs, most cockles mature at the age of two years. The lifespan can exceed ten years although few survive longer than 2–3 years. The sexes are separate and reproduction occurs in early summer. Very large numbers of larvae are released into the sea and these are at first free-living, before settling on the beach in June. Most successful settlement is in areas of reduced tidal flow, but subsequent growth in these areas is poor, presumably because of a reduced food supply. The cockle is exploited for food by Man.

Hancock (1971) presents data from a population study of the cockle in the Burry Inlet, South Wales, from 1958–1970. Population estimates were obtained from systematic samples taken along fixed line transects each November and May (Table XVI). Numbers reached a minimum of 367 million in May 1963 as a result of very high mortalities during the severe winter of 1962–63, but this was followed by exceptionally good recruitment, so that the highest total population (10,729 million) was recorded in November 1963. This peak can be followed through the subsequent years, so that 2019 million two-year olds occurred in May 1965. In these data, all cockles older than two years were grouped, because in most years their numbers were low. The main object of the

Table XVI. Summary of the population estimates of cockles in the Burry Inlet
(Numbers in millions)

	Numbers in May			Numbers in November		
	1-yr olds	2-yr olds	Older	1st Winter	2nd Winter	Older
1958	455	100	167	2837	76	154
1959	1667	40	92	2578	922	72
1960	1112	204	72	4967	901	164
1961	1472	153	116	3296	846	155
1962	1637	212	114	2648	1071	282
1963	102	204	61	10615	10	104
1964	4954	6	52	194	3192	40
1965	54	2019	38	5717	33	1775
1966	1249	20	1148	313	414	1033
1967	87	174	727	4169	49	652
1968	2278	34	513	800	1580	348
1969	362	1109	265	1213	229	796
1970	682	150	409			

N.B. The figures underlined show the shrinkage of successive age classes of cockles recruited during the summer of 1958.

study was to understand what factors determine survival to the adult stage (i.e. 2-year olds) since these are of a fishable size.

A number of mortality factors have been identified by Hancock and Urquhart (1965). Very severe winters are responsible for very high death-rates, particularly amongst cockles younger than those in their second winter. The severe winter of 1962–63 killed 96·1% of the first winter cockles, compared with 80·9% of the second-winter and 78·3% of older cockles. The precise cause of death is uncertain, but January and February 1963 were exceedingly cold with mean minimum air temperatures of $-2·5°C$ at nearby Swansea (Crisp, 1964).

Extremes of high temperature can also cause high death-rates at periods of exposure at low tide. At very high and very low temperatures, wave action can dislodge cockles, when their speed of digging is reduced.

The edible cockle is attacked by a wide range of parasites, but it is uncertain whether any plays an important role in its population dynamics. *Cercaria bucephalopsis haimeana* (Trematoda) causes parasitic castration in cockles and occurred in up to 12% of the Burry Inlet cockles. Metacercaria of a second trematode (*Meiogymnophallus minutus*) occurred in 100% of cockles over one year old, but whether this parasite ever causes the death of cockles is unknown.

D

Of the wide range of predators feeding on cockles, by far the most important is the oystercatcher (*Haematopus ostralegus*). Very large flocks of this bird feed in the Burry Inlet during autumn and winter. These have their maximum effect during November and December, since the adult birds start to leave during January for their breeding grounds in the North. A single oystercatcher may eat 2–300 cockles in a day, and their effect is made all the more conspicuous by their habit of leaving piles of shells on the beach. They feed mainly on second-winter cockles, although their predation on younger stages may be important, but less noticeable, because these are eaten in situ. Compared with the oystercatcher, other predators such as other sea birds, the shore crab (*Carcinus maenas*), and the flounder (*Platichthys flesus*) are unimportant.

There are very big variations from year to year in recruitment of young cockles to the population. Unfortunately, no data were obtained for egg production in each year and the larval stages could not be studied. It is possible however, to obtain a very rough estimate of the number of eggs produced each year from variations in the mean size of cockles in the population. Kristensen (1957) showed that there is a good correlation between shell length and the number of eggs per female cockle. By using Kristensen's figures and data for mean size of cockles taken by fishermen (Hancock, 1971; Hancock and Franklin, 1972), I have estimated the mean number of eggs per cockle for each year (Table XVII). In this calculation I have assumed an equal number of males

Table XVII. Showing the estimated recruitment of cockles to the Burry Inlet population

	No. of femal cockles (2 yr + in age) $\times 10^6$	Mean no. eggs/♀♀	Total no. eggs laid $\times 10^9$	Total young cockles settled (November) $\times 10^6$
1959	66	17500	1155	2578
1960	138	10500	1449	4967
1961	135	14250	1924	3296
1962	163	11750	1915	2648
1963	132	9000	1188	10615
1964	29	12750	370	194
1965	1029	13750	14149	5717
1966	564	17000	9588	313
1967	451	16750	7554	4169
1968	274	20000	5480	800
1969	687	20500	14084	1213

and females to be present in the population. There are undoubtedly large errors involved in this computation, but the estimates produced clearly demonstrate the vast numbers of larvae produced each year, and the small and variable proportion of these which succeed in settling successfully.

There is a marked inverse relationship between the number of young settling and the density of cockles already present (Fig. 33, $r = 0.7654$,

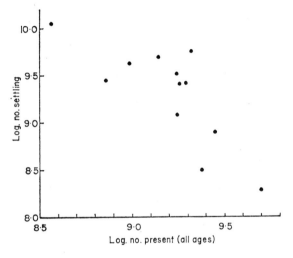

Fig. 33: The relationship between the number of young cockles settling and the density of those already present.

$P < 0.01$). Recruitment tends to be poor in years when the number of cockles already present is high. The reason for this is uncertain. Hancock (1971) suggests that larvae and older cockles will compete for food, and older cockles are known to inhale and kill larvae and newly settled young (Kristensen, 1957). More important perhaps is the fact that the young may find insufficient space to survive and grow between existing cockles when these are at high density (Hancock, 1971).

Intra-specific competition for food and space probably occur in local areas of overcrowding. Growth rates are inversely related to density (Hancock, 1969) and at very high densities cockles become stunted and deformed from growing against each other. Since fecundity is dependent upon size, fecundity is also inversely related to density.

The results from a k-factor analysis of the population data are shown in Fig. 34. In this, the maximum potential fecundity is taken as 21,000 eggs/♀♀. Total loss (K) is correlated with success in settling, k_1

$(r = 0.6522)$; with first-winter mortality, k_2 $(r = 0.7393)$, and with second-summer mortality, k_3 $(r = 0.6959)$. Loss in fecundity due to small size (k_0) and second-winter mortality (k_4) contribute little to variations in K. There appears then to be no single key factor operating on this population.

The mortality prior to settling (k_1) is correlated with the logarithm of the number of eggs produced $(r = 0.6699, P < 0.05)$, but the two-way regression test of initial on final density fails to prove that this loss

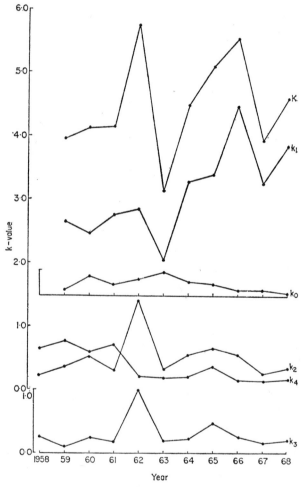

Fig. 34: A k-factor analysis of the population data for the edible cockle. $k_0 =$ Failure to reach maximum fecundity; $k_1 =$ Failure to settle; $k_2 =$ First winter mortality; $k_3 =$ Second summer mortality; $k_4 =$ Second winter mortality.

is density-dependent. This relationship probably results from both the number of eggs produced and the number of larvae settling being dependent upon the number of cockles already present in the population.

There has been a considerable controversy about the probable impact that oystercatchers have on the catch of cockles by fishermen. Oystercatchers are certainly competing directly with fishermen, since they both take the same sized prey. Hancock (1971) estimated that oystercatchers took more cockles during some winters than fishermen did during the full year. This has led to demands by cockle fishermen for the control of oystercatcher numbers. It is interesting to find however, that the mortality of cockles during their second winter (k_4), which is the age group predominantly taken by oystercatchers, is not correlated with the number of oystercatchers present. This suggest that the number of cockles surviving their second winter depends upon some factor other than predation by these birds. Also, k_4 had little effect upon total generation loss, so that it is unlikely that oystercatchers have much impact on trends in the cockle population.

Although this species has a very different way of life to the insects which we have so far considered, its population dynamics has much in common with them. Population size in the cockle appears to be limited by intra-specific competition for food and space. This has a marked effect on growth rates and on fecundity. The recruitment of young cockles to the population is dependent upon the size of the existing population of cockles. Again intra-specific competition for space, and possibly for food, appears to limit recruitment. No single factor appears to be sufficiently density-dependent to stabilize the population below the level where recruitment is impaired. From the data in Fig. 33 this level is probably in the order of 1500 million cockles (log. $= 9.3$).

Prior to the severe winter of 1962–63 recruitment varied comparatively little. The exceptionally high death-rate during that year however, allowed a huge recruitment to occur in the following summer. By the following year, the survivors of this 1963 recruitment were sufficiently numerous to prevent settlement of larvae, and recruitment in 1964 was the lowest recorded (Table XVI). Many of the 1963 year-class had died by 1965 and this allowed a high recruitment again. Subsequently, alternate years have been good and poor for recruitment, although the differences are smoothing out because some cockles live longer than two years. In this species, intra-specific competition for space appears to result in a greater stability than intra-specific competition for food produced in the cinnabar moth (see p. 68). In the cockle, intra-specific competition for space results in the death of only the very young stages. Once they are established into the population their length of life is very much longer than that of the insects which we have considered. This in itself leads to greater stability of the population when viewed on an annual time scale.

V. The Wood Pigeon

One of the best studies of a herbivorous bird is that of the wood pigeon (*Columba palumbus*) living in agricultural habitats in England. A population of this species has been studied by Murton, Isaacson and Westwood since 1959 in an area of 2647 ac (1072 ha) of farmland at Carlton in Cambridgeshire (Murton, 1965, 1974a; Murton *et al.*, 1966, 1974). They have kindly allowed me to carry out a *k*-factor analysis on data which they have in press (Murton, 1974b).

In more extensively wooded areas, this species feeds mainly upon acorns, beech mast and the buds of trees, but in the Carlton area the woods contain few oak and beech trees and the pigeons are almost totally dependent upon agricultural crops for their food. Cereals are the most important food during summer and autumn, but in winter, when grain is scarce, the birds feed mainly on clover leaves (*Trifolium pratense* and *T. repens*). When these are covered by snow, brassica crops become an important source of food.

Nesting occurs in woods and hedges and the species has a very long breeding season, from late March to October. There is a peak in breeding in mid-summer however, and most young coincide with the time of the grain harvest. The normal clutch is of two eggs and a maximum of five broods can be raised in a season. The adult birds feed their young on seeds, mainly grain, and a secretion of the crop known as "pigeon milk" which is rich in protein. Territorial behaviour occurs around the nesting site, but not on the feeding grounds. Incubation takes eighteen days and the young stay in the nest for just over three weeks.

Adult and juvenile birds feed in mixed flocks, particularly outside the breeding season, and at night they roost in woodland. It is during the winter that there is the greatest loss of birds, since food is frequently in short supply and many birds either die of starvation or emigrate. At these times juvenile birds tend to be displaced from food by adults, due to a marked social hierarchy in the feeding flocks (see p. 36) (Murton, 1971; Murton *et al.*, 1971). The number of birds which survive between the end of the breeding season and the beginning of December is correlated with the availability of grain (Murton *et al.*, 1974). During winter months mortality depends upon the number of birds which the grain supplies have allowed to survive and the amount of clover present. That losses during these two periods are due largely to starvation is indicated

Table XVIII. k-factor analysis of population data for the wood pigeon

	1939	1960	1961	1962	1963	1964	1965	1966	1967	1968	1969	1970
No. birds breeding	74	64	51	64	41	49	41	77	80	44	26	18
Max potential natality	370	320	255	320	205	245	205	385	400	220	130	90
Log	2·5682	2·5051	2·4065	2·5051	2·3118	2·3892	2·3118	2·5855	2·6021	2·3424	2·1139	1·9542
Actual no. eggs	237	178	131	146	109	111	103	199	173	120	54	49
Log	2·3747	2·2504	2·1173	2·1644	2·0374	2·0453	2·0128	2·2989	2·2380	2·0792	1·7324	1·6902
No. hatching	101	99	82	108	71	71	66	134	120	72	21	11
Log	2·0043	1·9956	1·9138	2·0334	1·8513	1·8513	1·8195	2·1271	2·0792	1·8573	1·3222	1·0414
No. chicks fledged	97	88	79	100	60	63	58	101	106	55	17	10
Log	1·9868	1·9445	1·8976	2·0000	1·7782	1·7993	1·7634	2·0043	2·0253	1·7404	1·2304	1·000
No. juveniles in Feb/March	4	20	9	5	15	12	39	19	8	2	15	
Log	0·6021	1·3010	0·9542	0·6990	1·1761	1·0792	1·5911	1·2788	0·9031	0·3010	1·1761	
No. juveniles in Apr/June	16	13	11	2	19	13	42	21	11	2	5	
Log	1·2041	1·1139	1·0414	0·3010	1·2788	1·1139	1·6232	1·3222	1·0414	0·3010	0·6990	
k_0 (Failure to lay max no. eggs)	0·1935	0·2547	0·2892	0·3407	0·2744	0·3439	0·2990	0·2866	0·3641	0·2632	0·3815	0·2640
k_1 (Egg mortality)	0·3704	0·2548	0·2035	0·1310	0·1861	0·1940	0·1933	0·1718	0·1588	0·2219	0·4102	0·6488
k_2 (Chick mortality)	0·0175	0·0511	0·0162	0·0334	0·0731	0·0520	0·0561	0·1228	0·0539	0·1169	0·0918	0·0414
k_3 (Winter mortality)	1·3847	0·6435	0·9434	1·3010	0·6021	0·7201	0·1723	0·7255	1·1222	1·4394	0·0543	
k_4 (Spring mortality)	−0·6020	0·1871	−0·0872	0·3980	−0·1027	−0·0347	−0·0321	−0·0434	−0·1383	0·0000	0·4771	
K (Total Loss)	1·3641	1·3912	1·3651	2·2041	1·0330	1·2753	0·6886	1·2633	1·5607	2·0414	1·4149	

by the higher proportion of birds which were found to have empty crops and to weigh less than 450 g in years when food was in short supply (Murton *et al.*, 1966).

Prior to the mid-1960s, farmers carried out pigeon control by shooting flocks coming into woodland to roost during the winter months. It was found however, that this had very little effect on pigeon numbers, since it simply killed many birds which would have died anyway from starvation. For this reason, the Ministry of Agriculture removed the subsidy on the cost of cartridges for pigeon control in 1965 (Murton *et al.*, 1974).

The importance of the supply of winter food in determining pigeon numbers is further seen in the changes in the status of the species in recent years. Throughout the country the wood pigeon has declined in abundance during the past five years. This is reflected in the population data from the Carlton area. Between 1959–68 the breeding population of pigeons fluctuated between 40–80/100 ac (Table XVIII). Since then however, numbers have been far lower, with only 16–26 birds/100 ac present from 1969–1973 (Murton, 1973). This has been brought about by changes in agricultural practices. First, since the mid-1960s there has been a shift away from the four-year rotation of crops to continuous cereal growing with no undersowing of clover. Next, many pastures and leys have been ploughed and put under barley, which is now used for feeding stock animals, and this has resulted in a further reduction in the total area of clover. Lastly, stubble burning is now a common practice and this reduces the amount of grain left after the crop has been harvested. All of these changes have reduced the availability of winter food and this has resulted in a decline in the numbers of the wood pigeon, in spite of the fact that winter shooting of the birds has been reduced.

Table XVIII shows the changes in the Carlton population of wood pigeons from 1959–1970. The maximum potential natality has been calculated by multiplying the number of pairs by ten, this being the maximum possible fecundity for one season. The results from a k-factor analysis of these data can be seen in Fig. 35. The key-factor determining trends from one year to the next is k_3 (winter loss), since this is closely correlated with total K ($r = 0.7020$). Total loss (K) is not closely correlated with any other k-factor. There is little variation in k_0 (failure to lay full potential of eggs). Egg mortality (k_1) is more variable and is due mainly to predation, particularly by jays (*Garrulus glandarius*). Eggs are normally taken only when the nest is unoccupied by the parent bird; at times of food shortage when the bird needs to leave the nest to feed, or when the bird is disturbed by humans or by birds from adjacent nests. When nest densities are high, there are frequent disputes between

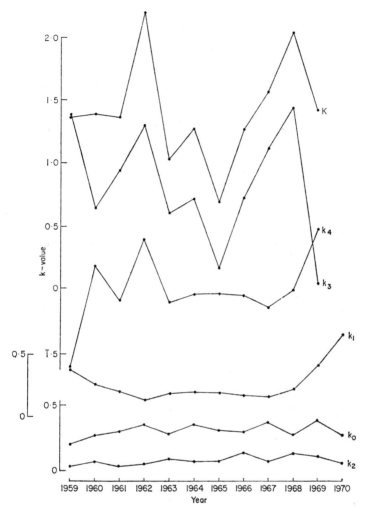

Fig. 35: A *k*-factor analysis of the population data for the wood pigeon in Table XVIII. k_0 = Failure to lay full potential; k_1 = Egg mortality; k_2 = Chick mortality; k_3 = Winter mortality; k_4 = Spring loss.

adjacent pairs, and this leaves the nest open to predation. Egg mortality (k_1) is closely related to density (Fig. 36). In 1969 and 1970 a pigeon shooting experiment was undertaken during the summer and this left many nests unguarded, so that predation was high. In 1962, 1966 and 1967, on the other hand, game keepers killed many of the predators in Carlton Wood and so predation was low (Murton *et al.*, 1974). In all

other years predation was not interferred with and for these years there
is a positive correlation between k_1 and density ($r = 0.9557, P < 0.001$,
$b = 0.4649$). The two-way regression test of initial and final densities
for these seven years shows that k_1 is density-dependent (Fig. 7, p. 20).
Egg mortality has very little effect on the population however, since
eggs which are lost are soon replaced by further laying. Added to this,
k_1 acts before the main disturbing influence of k_3 (winter mortality) so
that it can have little or no stabilizing effect.

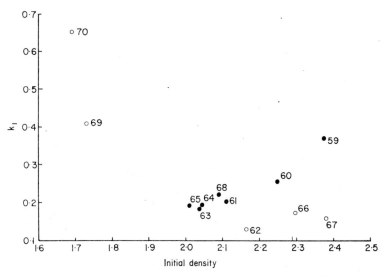

Fig. 36: The relationship between egg mortality (k_1) and density. ●, years when predation was not interferred with. ○, years when predators were controlled or adult
pigeons were shot.

Chick mortality (k_2) is caused mainly by starvation, particularly during
the early part of the season, before grain becomes available. Chicks are
rarely taken by predators and k_2 shows no density dependence.

Winter mortality (k_3) is significantly correlated with density ($r =
0.6299, P < 0.05$) but the two-way correlation test fails to prove density
dependence. As we have seen, winter mortality is caused primarily by
intra-specific competition for food, so that the relationship between
k_3 and density is probably not linear but is exponential (Fig. 37).

The final k-factor (k_4) is the loss between February and the start of
breeding. In many years this is negative, due to an immigration of young
birds into the study area during spring. k_4 includes the effect of territorial behaviour for nesting sites, and it is interesting to see that it shows

no density dependence. Clearly breeding territories are not a limiting resource in this population of the wood pigeon (see Chapter 4).

Murton (1961) has published data on the recovery of ringed wood pigeons, from which a time-specific life table for adult birds can be

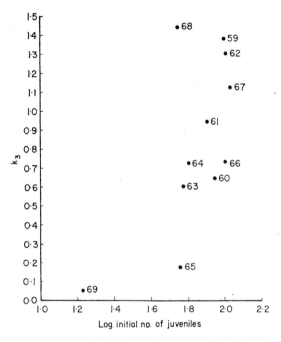

Fig. 37: The relationship between winter mortality (k_3) and density.

constructed (Table XIX). From this it can be seen that adult birds have an expectation of life of about two years, when once they have survived the first year. These data may under-estimate the chance of survival during the first year, since 78% of the recoveries were from shot birds, and young adults are more easily shot than older birds. The oldest wood pigeon so far recovered was in its fourteenth year.

This population of the wood pigeon makes an interesting comparison with that of the cinnabar moth described on pp. 63-75. Both populations regularly reach densities at which their food supplies become inadequate and starvation kills many individuals. This wood pigeon population has only fluctuated about four-fold during twelve years, whereas the moth fluctuated about 240-fold during eight years. Undoubtedly the main difference between these two species lies in the type of interaction

Table XIX. Time-specific life table for adult wood pigeons
(Murton 1961)

Age (x)	No. (lx)	No. dying (dx)	% dying (qx)	Expectation of life (ex)
0–1	58	37	64	1·4
1–2	21	8	38	2·0
2–3	13	3	23	1·9
3–4	10	6	60	1·3
4–5	4	0	0	1·5
5+	4	4	100	0·5

which occurs between individuals during intra-specific competition.
The cinnabar moth caterpillars interact by a scramble-type of competition in which all individuals continue feeding until the food supply
runs out. In some years all individuals will obtain some food, but most
will obtain insufficient to complete their development. Competition
in the wood pigeon is not so wasteful since a social hierarchy exists
within feeding flocks and the dominant individuals are normally assured
of obtaining enough food. For this reason, intra-specific competition for
food has far less catastrophic effects on population size in the pigeon
than in the moth.

As with the populations of other species described in this chapter, no
density-dependent factor can be identified which is capable of preventing
intra-specific competition from occurring. Predation by jays on eggs of
the pigeon is density-dependent, but this has little effect upon population
stability because it acts before the main disturbing influence of winter
mortality. Added to this, any loss from predation tends to be made good
by the birds' ability to lay replacement clutches of eggs.

VI. The Tawny Owl

There have been very few long-term studies of vertebrate predators. This
is mainly due to the fact that they tend to occur at such low densities
that very large areas must be covered to sample a reasonably sized
population. An exception to this is the tawny owl (*Strix aluco*) since this
lives at comparatively high densities within discrete populations in
open woodland. This is a nocturnal predator feeding mainly on small
mammals. In Britain it is resident throughout the year, that is it is
non-migratory, and it is strongly territorial.

Southern (1970) studied a population of this owl in Wytham Woods, Oxford, for a total of thirteen years. Wytham Woods are an area of mixed woodland, mainly deciduous, covering an area of 1300 ac (525 ha). Within this area, Southern was able to census the territory-holding adults each year just before the breeding season, by means of the birds' noisy calling during territorial challenges.

Tawny owls normally nest in large tree-holes, but Southern found that they readily occupied specially designed nesting boxes. A mirror fixed at an angle at the entrance to the box enabled an observer to see inside without having to climb the tree. It was also possible to floodlight the box entrance with red light and so to identify prey brought to the nestlings by direct observation from a hide.

Breeding begins in March and the young are fledged about mid-May, after which they remain dependent on their parents for food until about August. Since they cry loudly for food it is easy to census them at this time.

The diet of the owls was studied throughout the year by an analysis of the bones in pellets which are ejected by owls after feeding. This tended to be done at set perching posts which could be visited regularly and cleared of pellets. The main prey in Wytham Woods proved to be the wood mouse (*Apodemus sylvaticus*) and the bank vole (*Clethrionomys glareolus*), which together made up about 60% of the vertebrates eaten (Southern, 1954). These were in about equal proportions. Also taken were short-tailed voles (*Microtus agrestis*), common shrews (*Sorex araneus*), moles (*Talpa europaea*), as well as small birds, insects and earthworms. The tawny owl hunts by dropping onto its prey from a low branch. It locates its prey mainly by sound.

Changes in the population of territory-holding adults are shown in Table XX. In 1947 there were only seventeen pairs of owls. This was after a very hard winter, when there was a prolonged period of deep snow, and many owls were known to have died from starvation. During the next nine years the population slowly built up to thirty-two pairs in 1956, after which it remained steady. Although the number of territory-holding adults did not vary much, there was far more variation in the number which attempted to breed. This ranged from twenty-two pairs in 1959 to none in 1958. Years in which few attempted to breed were years when prey numbers were particularly low (Table XX). The mean number of eggs per clutch also varied with the availability of prey, from 2·0–2·9 eggs per clutch. Table XX, also shows the number of young fledged in each year. This ranged from 0–1·3 chicks per territory.

If we look at the detailed losses of eggs we find that most failed to hatch because of desertion and chilling. During incubation the male

Table XX. The breeding success of tawny owls in Wytham Woods

Year	No. pairs	No. pairs breeding	Mean clutch	No. eggs	No. young fledged	Log. No. rodents/12 acres in June
1947	17	11	2·5	27	20	—
1948	20	13	2·0	26	20	—
1949	20	18	2·8	50	26	1·7
1950	20	17	2·6	44	25	1·9
1951	21	12	2·1	25	6	1·5
1952	24	17	2·5	42	21	2·2
1953	24	15	2·0	30	20	1·7
1954	26	18	2·5	45	17	1·9
1955	30	4	2·0	8	4	1·4
1956	32	21	2·2	46	24	1·8
1957	32	20	2·9	58	20	2·6
1958	31	0	0·0	0	0	1·0
1959	32	22	2·4	53	28	2·4

bird must provide food for the female. When this is scarce, or when bad weather makes hunting difficult, the female may be forced to leave the nest, and then the eggs became chilled. There was some laying of replacement clutches in those years when food was abundant during the early summer.

The availability of food and the effects of weather also play a part in determining mortality of nestlings. Generally, it is the smallest bird in the brood which dies during periods of food shortage, i.e. that which hatched last.

After fledging, the young birds remain dependent on their parents for food until August. After that they can hunt for themselves and they then tend to disperse. There is little mortality up to the time when they leave the territory, but little is known about their survival after that.

A life-table for adult birds can be built up from the recovery of birds which were ringed as nestlings. This shows that there was a heavy loss during the first year, but that after that the expectation of life was from 2–3 years (Table XXI).

The results of a k-factor analysis of these data are shown in Fig. 38. Failure to breed (k_0) contributes most to total generation loss (K) ($r = 0.7355$) and it probably represents the key-factor determining generation success. Variation in clutch size (k_1) follows the same pattern, while failure of the eggs to hatch (k_2) is large and rather variable. Nestling mortality (k_3) appears to contribute little, but overwinter loss (k_4)

Table XXI. Time-specific life table for adult tawny owls in Wytham Wood

Age (x)	No. (lx)	No. dying (dx)	% dying (qx)	Expectation of life (ex)
0–1	19	10	53	2·1
1–2	9	2	21	2·9
2–3	7	1	14	2·6
3–4	6	1	17	2·0
4–5	5	1	20	1·3
5+	4	4	100	0·5

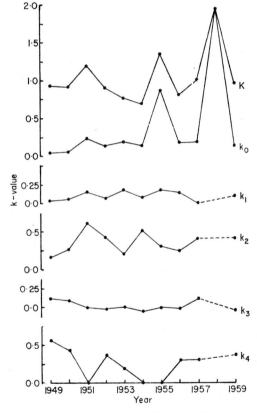

Fig. 38: The k-factor analysis of the population data for the tawny owl. k_0 = Failure to breed; k_1 = Variation in clutch size; k_2 = Egg mortality; k_3 = Nestling Mortality; k_4 = Overwinter loss. (Dr. H. N. Southern has kindly pointed out an error in his published figure for Total K, 1954 (Southern, 1970).)

tends to be compensatory in its action, by showing a reverse trend to k_0 and k_1.

Success in laying and hatching eggs is determined by the abundance of mice and voles, but above a density of 100/12 ac (4·8 ha) the numbers of these prey are no longer limiting (Fig. 39). Although k_2 follows the same trend as k_0 and k_1, this relationship is obscured by the effects of weather on the ability of the owls to catch enough prey. There is a

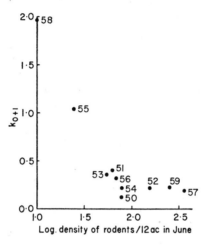

Fig. 39: The effect of prey numbers on the success in laying and hatching of eggs (k_{0+1}) by the tawny owl.

significant positive correlation between k_2 (failure to hatch) and the number of rainy days during incubation (Fig. 40; $r = 0.8195, P < 0.01$).

Overwintering loss (k_4) covers the period between the young leaving the nests and the adults starting to breed in the following year. It therefore includes both mortality and emigration. Losses before fledging (k_{0-3}) are usually insufficient to bring numbers down to the level where they just replace adults which die. Since however, the number of adults does not vary much between years, k_4 tends to be related to density ($r = 0.7768, P < 0.01$). The two-way regression test does not prove k_4 to be density-dependent however. The reason for this can be seen in Fig. 41, since the relationship between k_4 and density clearly is not linear. Instead, the relationship is more like a typical competition curve (see p. 24) in which loss becomes density-dependent only above a certain density. This suggests that density dependence is brought about at higher densities by intra-specific competition for territories. Any individuals in excess of the number of territories are forced to emigrate.

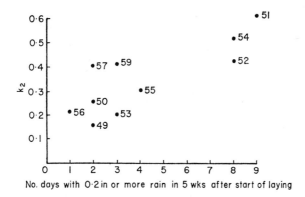

Fig. 40: The effect of wet weather on egg mortality (k_2) in the tawny owl.

Precisely what happens to these excess birds is uncertain, but it seems likely that some survive in less suitable habitats, since in some years territory holders which die are replaced by birds which immigrate from elsewhere. This happened in 1951, 1955, and 1958, when very few young were fledged in the study area.

The tawny owl is a relatively long lived bird; at the end of the first year it has an expectation of life of about 3 years (Table XXI). Its innate capacity of increase is generally low however. The population built up very slowly between 1947–56. This is because reproduction is

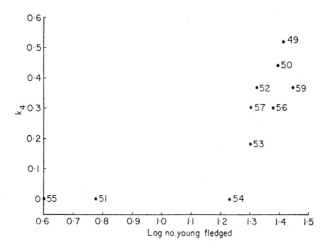

Fig. 41: The relationship between overwinter loss (k_4) and density in the tawny owl.

so dependent upon an adequate supply of rodent prey. The limiting density of these appears to be in the order of 100/12 ac (4·8 ha) and at this density it is unlikely that intra-specific competition for food ever occurs among the owls. In other words, it is a relative, rather than an absolute shortage of prey which limits reproduction (see p. 23). One owl catching a prey is unlikely to make any difference to the availability of prey to other owls. Population size is however, ultimately limited by intra-specific competition, but for territories, not for food.

The mean size of a territory after the population had levelled off (i.e. 1955–9) differed in different parts of the Wytham estate. It was about 30 ac (12 ha) in closed woodland, but was about 50 ac (20 ha) in more open woodland. Much smaller territories were recorded, down to about 10 ac (4 ha) but the birds failed to breed in these. The mean size of territory gradually decreased during the course of the population build-up, but the size did not appear to be influenced by year to year fluctuations in the numbers of rodents. In other words, territory size did not appear to be determined primarily by food supply.

What then is the function of territory in the tawny owl? Southern (1970) suggests that the ownership of a territory is advantageous in ensuring the possession of familiar hunting grounds. As he points out however, this does not explain why territories differ in size in different habitats within Wytham Woods. Certainly, a territory is required by tawny owls to breed, but the reason for this is not yet clear.

VII. Conclusions

From these six case histories some generalizations can be made. First, it is clear that the key-factor determining population trends can act at any stage in the life cycle of an animal. Thus it operates at the beginning of each generation in the tawny owl (failure to breed) and at the end of each generation in the wood pigeon (winter mortality of juvenile birds). In some species the key-factor is intra-specific competition for resources, such as food (wood pigeon) and space (cockle), but other factors, such as natural enemies (*Phytodecta*) and weather (cockle), can also act in this way.

The second generalization is that for many species the upper limits of population size are determined by intra-specific competition. In four out of six studies (i.e. cinnabar moth, edible cockle, wood pigeon and tawny owl) competition limited population growth, while in the pine looper there was evidence to suggest that this also applied in some populations. It must be remembered however, that ecologists tend to study those species that are numerous and for this reason, it is possible that these studies do not reflect the normal rate of occurrence of competition in animal populations.

The impact which intra-specific competition has depends on the type of resource for which there is competition and the type of interaction that occurs between individuals in the population. Competition for food (cinnabar moth, wood pigeon) can result in death of large numbers of individuals, while competition for territory (tawny owl) may have far less disastrous results. Scramble competition (cinnabar) results in larger fluctuations in population size than contest competition (wood pigeon, tawny owl).

The lower limit of population size is likely to be extinction, since in none of these studies was any factor found which was sufficiently density-dependent to prevent extinction. On the other hand, the statistical proof of density dependence is extremely difficult from field data, especially since many density-related processes are not linear in their response. Only two examples were found in which density dependence could be proved by the two-way regression test of initial on final density, but in neither case was the factor capable of stabilizing the population. *Beauveria* was acting this way on adult broom beetles, but its action was masked by density-independent, contemporaneous mortality from the parasite *Periletus*. The other example of a linear density-dependent relationship was the predation of wood pigeon eggs by jays. This however, had little effect on the population because it acted before the key factor (winter mortality) and because replacement eggs were laid so readily.

Lastly in both populations in which intra-specific competition was **not** found to occur (pine looper, broom beetle) natural control appeared to be brought about by a large array of density-independent factors, rather than by any one density-dependent factor.

9. Population Cycles

One of the most fascinating, unsolved puzzles in population ecology concerns the cause of the regular, cyclic fluctuations in population size which occur in some species. The most famous example of these is the Norwegian lemming (*Lemmus lemmus*) which migrates in vast numbers from its sub-alpine mountain habitats every 3–4 years. These huge, down-hill migrations result in enormous numbers drowning when they reach the sea, and this has led to many widely accepted legends suggesting that they commit suicide. The first dated account of a lemming migration was in 1579, when they were described "falling from the sky", and since 1862 well documented accounts show a remarkable regularity in "lemming years", every 3–4 years (Elton, 1942).

The best established cycles occur in populations of northern-hemisphere birds and mammals, although they undoubtedly also occur in other animals. The most common cycles show a periodicity of either 3–4 years, as in the lemming, or of 9–10 years. A 3–4 year cycle has been demonstrated for various arctic rodents, arctic fox (*Alopex lagopus*), snowy owl (*Nyctea nyctea*) and a number of game birds. Species with a well marked 9–10 years cycle include the snowshoe rabbit (*Lepus americanus*), musk rat (*Ondatra zibethica*), Canadian lynx (*Lynx canadensis*), ruffed grouse (*Bonasa umbellus*) and atlantic salmon (*Salmo salar*). Some species, e.g. the willow grouse (*Lagopus lagopus*), exhibit a 3–4 year cycle and a 9–10 year cycle in different parts of their distribution (Williams, 1954). Siivonen (1948) has suggested that the longer cycle (10 year) is made up of three short cycles (average $3\frac{1}{3}$ years) in which the third cycle has a greater amplitude than the other two. Thus these types of cycle could be determined by a single cyclic phenomenon. Cycles of different length have been demonstrated for other animals however, e.g. a 5–6 year cycle for the red grouse (*Lagopus lagopus scoticus*) in Britain (Mackenzie, 1952) and a 7–8 year cycle for the larch tortrix moth (*Zeiraphera griseana*) in Switzerland (Baltensweiler, 1968).

Although there is a general synchrony in numbers, local populations may be out of phase by a few years. MacLulich (1937) showed, for example, that peak populations of the snowshoe rabbit in Canada occurred earliest in coastal districts of the Maritimes and the St. Lawrence valley, southern British Columbia and the Mackenzie delta; and occurred latest in the interior of the continent. Williams (1954) found a similar pattern of abundance in the cycles of tetraonid game birds in North America.

There is often a well marked synchrony in the cycles of different species inhabiting the same region. The cycle for the willow-grouse appears to be synchronized with that of the snowshoe rabbit in North America, and with that of the lemming in Scandinavia (Williams, 1954). The cycles for predatory species, such as snowy owl, arctic fox, and Canadian lynx, are correlated with the cycles of their principal prey, but tend to lag slightly behind (Pitelka *et al.*, 1955). This can be seen for the Canadian lynx and the snowshoe rabbit in Fig. 42.

There have been a number of theories proposed to account for population cycles, but all have been found to be inadequate (Keith, 1963). Many of the earliest workers assumed that the cycles were caused by the intrinsic oscillations which the early mathematical theories of Lotka and Volterra (D'Ancona, 1954) and of Nicholson and Bailey (1935) predicted from the interaction of predator and prey populations. These theories had suggested that a single predator species attacking a single prey species in a limited area, with all external factors constant, automatically led to periodic oscillations in the numbers of both. As the predator population increased it consumed more prey, until the prey's numbers began to decrease. As this happened, less food was available to the predator which then declined in numbers, until it could no longer prevent the prey from increasing again, thus starting the cycle again. As we have seen in Chapter 6, the interactions between predators and prey are not as simple as this. Added to this, the numbers of some herbivores have been shown to cycle in the absence of predators. For example, the population of snowshoe rabbits on Valcour Island, New York, continued to cycle after predators had been eliminated from the island (Crissey and Darrow, 1949). Similarly, an introduced population of the snowshoe rabbit on Anticosti Island in Canada cycled in phase with populations on the mainland, in spite of the lynx being absent from the island (Elton and Nicholson, 1942). It is now clear that the herbivore

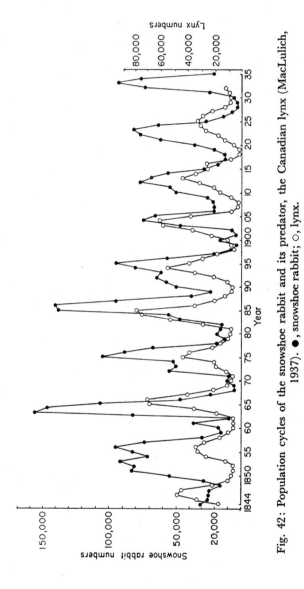

Fig. 42: Population cycles of the snowshoe rabbit and its predator, the Canadian lynx (MacLulich, 1937). ●, snowshoe rabbit; ○, lynx.

cycles are not brought about by the action of the predators. On the other hand, it is generally agreed that the predator cycles depend upon those of the herbivores. The former cycles are most marked in areas where the predator is feeding almost exclusively on the cycling population of a herbivore. In other words, it is the cycle in the predator's food supply which causes the cycle in its numbers.

The cause of the basic, herbivore cycles is more difficult to understand. An attractive hypothesis is that the herbivore cycles are dependent upon cycles in their food supply. During herbivore peaks the plants may be damaged by grazing to such an extent that they cannot recover until the herbivores' numbers drop. This is perhaps particularly possible in the Arctic, where many plants are unable to make luxuriant growth and to produce seed every year. Interactions between the populations of herbivores and of their food plants have been little studied, but the two can be closely dependent upon one another, as can be seen in Chapter 8, where fluctuations in the abundance of the cinnabar moth and its food plant, ragwort, are described. The main objection to this hypothesis is that, in contrast to the predatory species, there is little evidence of actual starvation during the crash in herbivore numbers.

Another hypothesis suggests that changes in the vigour of individuals occur during changes in population size, which perpetuate the cycle. As we saw in Chapters 3 and 5, there are often marked variations in the quality of individuals which are correlated with changes in population density; due either to stress from overcrowding, or to genotypic variations resulting from the different selection pressures at different densities. Cyclic changes in quality have been shown to occur in several species which show cycles in population density, but it is very difficult to determine whether these occur as a result of the population cycle, or whether they are causing the cycle. The role of these qualitative changes can only be assessed by intensive study of the dynamics of individual populations.

The synchrony between different populations of one species, and between the cycles of different species, has led several workers to attempt to correlate population cycles with patterns of weather. Such attempts have been made mainly with the sunspot cycle, since weather is affected by variations in solar radiations and sunspots have been measured over a long period of time (MacLagen, 1940; MacLulich, 1937). Such attempts to obtain correlations have failed however, and it is clear that if weather variations are causing these cycles, sunspot numbers do not adequately describe these variations.

It is unlikely that the cause of population cycles will be discovered until more intensive studies are made on populations which show this phenomenon. So far, too few have been made to generalize. The most thorough studies of cyclic populations are those on the larch tortrix (*Zeiraphera griseana*) and on the red grouse (*Lagopus lagopus scoticus*), neither of which shows the common 3–4 year or 9–10 year periodicity. More limited data are also available for the rock ptarmigan (*Lagopus mutus*) in Alaska.

I. The Larch Tortrix

The larch tortrix moth lives on various coniferous trees including larch (*Larix decidua*). In certain parts of the Alps its populations fluctuate enormously, so that in some years it causes widespread defoliation of

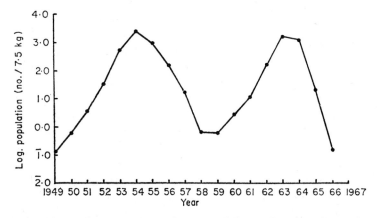

Fig. 43: Changes in the numbers of larch tortrix larvae (Baltensweiler, 1968).

its food plants. In the Engadin valley, Switzerland, the forest service has recorded defoliation of larch regularly during the past 100 years. If one assumes that peak population density coincides with the greatest defoliation, the moth's population cycles with a mean periodicity between peaks of 7·4 years (Baltensweiler, 1968). In other areas where extensive defoliation of larch occurs, the periodicity is not so regular as in the Engadin. Damage tends to be three of four years later in the Austrian Alps than in the western Alps, but older records suggest that this relationship was reversed during the last century.

Baltensweiler (loc. cit.) gives figures for the numbers of fourth instar larvae during eighteen years (Fig. 43). These show that the moth's density can change 20,000-fold within five generations. Cyclic outbreaks of this sort occur only at an altitude of 1700–2000m, in the interior of the Alps, or on their southern slopes. At lower altitudes, visible damage to larch is no longer cyclic, and at 800 m above sea level no defoliation has been recorded. In other words, there appears to be an optimum zone for the moth, which is determined by altitude. Although defoliation is not periodic below 1700 m, regular population cycles occur, possibly due to immigrations of adult moths from the optimum regions during peaks in abundance.

At low altitudes the moth's eggs hatch more or less simultaneously throughout the crown of the larch trees. Higher up, eggs exposed to direct sun hatch up to four weeks earlier than those in the shade. This leads to a more heterogeneous age structure at high altitudes, so that the population is less vulnerable to adverse weather. The young caterpillars feed within the short shoots of the larch and at higher altitudes part of the population always hatches synchronously with bud burst.

At periods of high density there is a shortage of fresh green food and intra-specific competition probably occurs. There is a high larval mortality at this time and surviving females have a reduced fecundity, so that fecundity is delayed density-dependent. At the time of the 1954 peak there was an epizootic of virus disease, but this was present at only low incidence in the following 1963–4 peak.

Baltensweiler concludes that weather conditions in the optimum zone permanently favour population growth. At the peak in numbers there is intra-specific competition for food, but this does not appear to be the only cause of the crash in numbers after the peak. A similar crash occurred in a DDT treated area, where defoliation had been prevented. This has led Baltensweiler to suggest that changes in quality in the moth may contribute to the cycle. There is a decrease in the proportion of completely black fifth-instar larvae and a corresponding increase of larvae of intermediate colour phases in the course of the cycle, but the ecological implications of these changes are not yet known.

II. The Red Grouse

The red grouse was at one time known as *Lagopus scoticus*, but it is now considered to be a sub-species of the willow grouse (*Lagopus lagopus*). The willow grouse has a circumpolar distribution and has a 9–10 year population cycle in North America and a 3–4 year cycle in north-west Europe. In Britain, the red grouse probably has a 5–6 year population cycle although the periodicity is not well marked in some areas. Here they are inhabitants of moorlands and they feed almost exclusively on heather (*Calluna vulgaris*).

The grouse raises one brood each year and the chicks are active from hatching and collect their own food, which at first consists partly of insects, along with vegetation. Breeding territories are taken up by cock birds in October or November and are held until late May. The more aggressive cocks have the largest territories.

Over base-rich rocks, the heather is more nutritive and grouse stocks tend to be larger, tend to fluctuate less in size and tend to have a better breeding success than over base-poor rocks (Moss, 1969). The birds feed selectively upon heather which has the highest nitrogen and phosphorus content and bigger broods can be obtained if the heather is given an application of fertiliser.

Jenkins *et al.* (1963) give the results of a five year study of a population of red grouse in north-east Scotland. The essential data from this study are summarized in Table XXII.

Table XXII. Variations in the numbers of red grouse in the low area of Glen Esk

	1957	1958	1959	1960	1961
No. of breeding females (April)	175	156	89	72	182
Mean weight ♀♀ (g)	612	587	578	618	614
Average clutch	7·9	6·9	6·1	8·1	7·8
No. of eggs laid	1383	1076	543	583	1420
% Hatch	77·4	68·2	64·4	83·5	76·3
No. of chicks hatched	1070	734	350	487	1083
% Survival	61·5	49·2	29·4	79·7	62·7
No. of young in August	658	361	103	388	679
Total young + old birds (August)	991	771	358	554	1027
Sex ratio (%♀♀)	45·3	42·2	28·8	43·7	46·0
No. birds shot	476	134	56	86	415

The size of the breeding stock is dependent upon the number of territories which are taken by cock birds in the autumn. Over the five years this ranged from 72–182 pairs. Very few birds migrate to breed elsewhere and most birds which fail to obtain a territory die during the winter (Jenkins *et al.*, 1967). Although there may be a number of causes of death amongst these birds (e.g. predation, accidents, etc.), they are often emaciated and heavily parasitised (see p. 44). Hens rarely breed for more than two successive years.

All moorland which is covered predominantly with heather is occupied by grouse each year, but the number and size of territories varies considerably. Territory size does not appear to be related to the amount of current year's growth on the heather (i.e. total food supply), although it may be related to variations in the nutritive value of the heather (Watson and Moss, 1972). Also, territory size does not depend mainly upon the density of competing birds. There are however, marked differences in the size of territories held by cocks reared at different times in the population cycle. Territorial cocks in year classes which hatch during the population decline appear to be more aggressive and take larger territories than other birds (Watson and Miller, 1971).

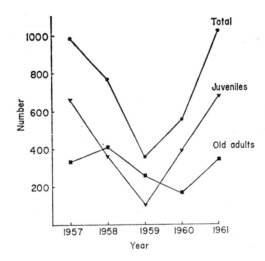

Fig. 44: Red grouse numbers in August of each year.

Breeding success is determined by parental condition in the spring, which in turn depends upon the state of the heather between autumn and spring. The number of young reared per pair is not related to territory size. The poor breeding in 1958 and 1959 (Table XXII) was associated with severe browning of the heather during the previous winters. In those years the females weighed less and on average laid a smaller clutch of eggs, than in the other years, when the heather was undamaged. In 1958 and 1959, hatchability of the eggs and subsequent survival of the chicks were low.

The cycles in abundance which have been recorded for this species are in the numbers of birds present in August, when shooting begins. This number is far more dependent upon the number of young birds produced in the current year than on the survival of old birds which have already bred (Fig. 44). A k-factor analysis has therefore been carried

Table XXIII. *k*-factor analysis of the data in Table XXII

	1957	1958	1959	1960	1961
Max potential natality (12 × No. ♀♀ in August of previous yr)	—	5387 (3·7314)	3904 (3·5915)	1237 (3·0923)	2905 (3·4631)
Max natality from survivors from shooting (12 × No. ♀♀ surviving)	—	2799 (3·4470)	3226 (3·5087)	1044 (3·0187)	2454 (3·3899)
Max natality from territory holders (12 × No. ♀♀ breeding)	2100 (3·3222)	1872 (3·2723)	1068 (3·0286)	864 (2·9365)	2184 (3·3393)
Actual No. eggs	1383 (3·1409)	1076 (3·0319)	543 (2·7348)	583 (2·7657)	1420 (3·1523)
No. hatching	1217 (3·0852)	734 (2·8657)	350 (2·5441)	487 (2·6875)	1083 (3·0345)
No. young in August	568 (2·8182)	361 (2·5575)	103 (2·0128)	388 (2·5888)	679 (2·8319)
k_0 (Shooting)	—	0·2844	0·0828	0·0736	0·0732
k_1 (Failure to obtain territory + winter mortality)	—	0·1747	0·4801	0·0822	0·0506
k_2 (Failure to lay max clutch)	0·1813	0·2404	0·2938	0·1708	0·1870
k_3 (Egg mortality)	0·0557	0·1662	0·1907	0·0782	0·1178
k_4 (Chick mortality)	0·2670	0·3082	0·5313	0·0987	0·2026
K (Total loss)	—	1·1739	1·5787	0·5035	0·6312

out on the data of Jenkins *et al.* (1963) to try to identify the key factor(s) causing variations in the August population of juveniles. The contribution made by variations in shooting (k_0), the number of territories (k_1), in clutch size (k_2), and in egg (k_3) and chick mortality (k_4) to total generation loss (K) can be seen in Table XXIII and Fig. 45. Watson (1971) has published a k-factor analysis of thirteen years data for the red grouse, but these data do not include figures for clutch size or for egg and chick mortality.

With the exception of k_0, all of the k-values calculated here appear to be correlated (Fig. 45), but chick mortality (k_4) and the failure of adults to obtain a territory (k_1) probably contribute most to total K. Clearly, data from more years are required to sort this out, but it seems likely that there is some factor which is affecting all of these k-values in the same way in different years. Both chick mortality and the aggressiveness of the young birds appear to be related to the condition of the parent birds in spring and to the size of the eggs which they lay. This in turn appears to depend upon the nutritive status of the food plants during winter and early spring (Watson and Moss, 1972), but it is not at all clear why this should vary in a cyclic manner.

III. The Rock Ptarmigan

The rock ptarmigan (*Lagopus mutus*) is closely related to the red grouse. It has a circumpolar distribution and tends to occur at higher altitudes than the grouse. Weeden and Theberge (1972) have published data for a population of *L. mutus* at Eagle Creek, Alaska, from 1960–1969. The abundance of this species shows cyclic fluctuations with a 10-year periodicity. This study was carried out on 15 square miles of arctic tundra on which the dominant plants were bilberry (*Vaccinium uliginosum*), birch (*Betula nana*) and willow (*Salix* spp.). During the summer, rock ptarmigan feed on a wide variety of plants, but in winter their feeding is restricted to birch buds.

In Alaska, the two sexes segregate during the winter. Most cock birds remain in flocks on the tundra, but hens form flocks at lower altitudes. Breeding territories are not occupied until late March, and although the birds are mainly monogamous, some males mate with more than one female. Eggs are laid in late May or early June and they hatch in about 3 weeks. The young chicks stay together as a family party but feed independently. Unsuccessful females rarely renest.

Weeden and Theberge (1972) carried out a k-factor analysis of their

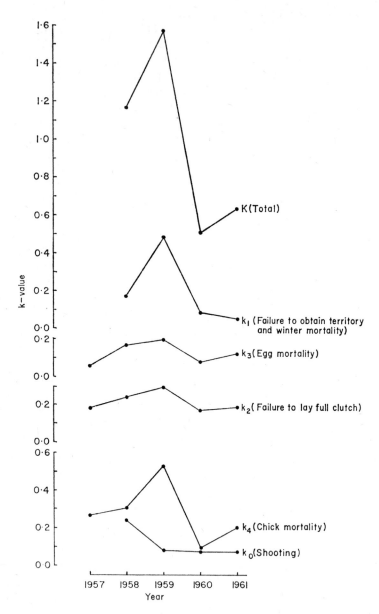

Fig. 45: A *k*-factor analysis of the red grouse data in Table XXII.

data, but unfortunately, like the analysis done by Watson (1971) for the red grouse, this was incorrectly done (see p. 20). Their data can however, be re-analysed by subtracting adult numbers from those of each of their age classes, so that single cohorts of progeny are dealt with separately. Since we are primarily interested in determining the factors causing the cycle in abundance of birds in autumn, this k-factor analysis has been made from August to August, as was done for the red grouse (p. 113). In the calculation of maximum potential natality, the sex ratio of birds in August is taken to be the same as that at the start of the breeding season (Table XXIV).

The results from the k-factor analysis are similar to those obtained for the red grouse, in that there is a tendency for all of the k-values (except k_4) to fluctuate in the same way (Fig. 46). k_3 ($r = 0.8516$) and k_0 ($r = 0.7185$) show the greatest correlation with total K. As with the red grouse, these data suggest that some factor is affecting the k-values in the same way in the different years.

Egg mortality (k_3) is due mainly to predation by weasels (*Mustela erminea*). In those nests which produced no young, 80% had eggs either damaged or taken by predators. Desertion was comparatively unimportant. If one graphs k_3 against the logarithm of egg numbers, the successive years form an anti-clockwise plot due to delayed density dependence (Fig. 47). This suggests that weasel numbers are dependent upon the abundance of ptarmigan eggs in the previous year and that variations in k_3 are probably the result of the population cycle rather than the cause of it.

k_0 includes the effect of territorial behaviour in spring and the loss of birds during the winter. The winter loss of birds, mainly juveniles, affected both sexes equally, although they occupy different habitats at this time of the year. Weeden and Theberge failed to demonstrate any correlation between winter loss and the amount of snow cover, so that it seems unlikely that snow limited food availability, even for males on the tundra. Prolonged icing of the vegetation occurred in only one year (1962–63). It is not known whether there were any variations in the nutritive quality of plants between years. Finally, hunting appeared to have little effect upon subsequent spring numbers.

Weeden and Theberge do not state whether there was a surplus of non-breeding birds each year, which would have indicated that there was competition for territories. In the red grouse a surplus was produced each year. Territory size varied considerably between years but it is unknown whether there was a cyclic change in the average aggressiveness of the birds. Weeden and Theberge (1972) conclude that qualitative changes of this sort must be occurring, since the cycle in abundance can

Table XXIV. *k*-factor analysis of population data for the rock ptarmigan

	1960	1961	1962	1963	1964	1965	1966	1967	1968	1969
Log. max potential natality (♀ × No. ♀♀ in August of previous yr)	—	3·3324	3·6077	3·5160	3·4050	3·3077	3·2472	3·3361	3·3881	3·4041
Log. max natality from territory holders (♀ × No. ♀♀ breeding)	2·8293	3·0845	3·1446	3·0294	2·9542	2·7324	2·8293	2·9542	2·9877	2·9754
Log. actual no. eggs	2·7889	2·9996	3·0355	2·9269	2·8195	2·6590	2·8293	2·9494	2·9360	2·8344
Log. no fertile eggs	2·7803	2·9727	3·0128	2·9133	2·7589	2·6365	2·8209	2·9405	2·8716	2·7482
Log. no. hatching	2·6990	2·9031	2·7520	2·6561	2·5172	2·5403	2·6972	2·8331	2·7042	2·5539
Log. no. young in August	2·4955	2·8293	2·6385	2·5038	2·4232	2·4548	2·5051	2·5944	2·5441	2·3856
k_0 (Failure to obtain territory)	—	0·2479	0·4631	0·4866	0·4508	0·5753	0·4179	0·3819	0·4004	0·4287
k_1 (Failure to lay full clutch)	0·0404	0·0849	0·1091	0·1025	0·1347	0·0734	0·0000	0·0048	0·0517	0·1410
k_2 (Infertility)	0·0086	0·0269	0·0227	0·0136	0·0606	0·0225	0·0084	0·0089	0·0644	0·0862
k_3 (Egg mortality)	0·0813	0·0696	0·2608	0·2572	0·2417	0·0962	0·1237	0·1074	0·1674	0·1943
k_4 (Chick mortality)	0·2035	0·0738	0·1135	0·1523	0·0940	0·0855	0·1921	0·2387	0·1601	0·1683
K (Total loss)	—	0·5031	0·9692	1·0122	0·9818	0·8529	0·7421	0·7417	0·8440	1·0185

not be related to any direct environmental cause, but so far such changes in quality have not been identified.

IV. Conclusions

The data from these detailed studies show certain similarities. Food supply and quality are important in determining the breeding success

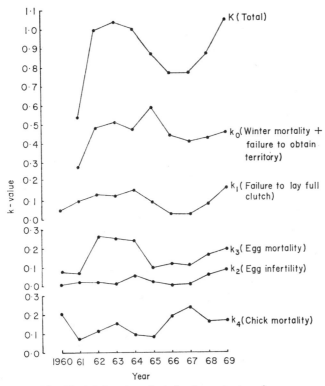

Fig. 46: A k-factor analysis for the rock ptarmigan.

and survival in both the larch tortrix and the red grouse. In the case of the tortrix there is an absolute shortage of green food due to defoliation by the caterpillars at the peaks in the cycle. In the red grouse there is not an absolute shortage of food, but the nutritive value of the heather varies considerably between years. Both the tortrix and the grouse show

E

qualitative changes in the individuals produced at different times of the cycle. The biological significance of these changes is uncertain in the larch tortrix, but in the red grouse these changes influence the competitive ability of cock birds in holding territories. Whether these changes are the

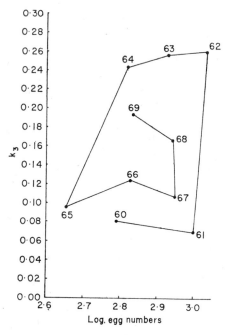

Fig. 47: The delayed density-dependent predation of rock ptarmigan eggs (k_3) by weasels.

result of differential survival at different times in the cycle, or whether they are themselves generating the cycle is uncertain, however. Clearly we are still a long way from understanding population cycles of this sort.

10. Population Theories

During the past forty years a number of theories have been proposed to describe the interaction between animal populations and their environments. Many of the earliest ideas grew out of practical experience obtained from attempts at the biological control of pests (e.g. Howard and Fiske, 1911; Smith, 1935), but from quite early on mathematical modelling greatly extended the field of theoretical study (Lotka, 1925; Volterra, 1926; Nicholson and Bailey, 1935). In this chapter I shall do no more than outline the more important ideas in population theory, as a framework for further reading. Good reviews can be found in Clark *et al.* (1967) and Bakker (1964).

By far the most comprehensive of the theories that have been proposed are those of Nicholson, of Andrewartha and Birch, and of Milne. These deserve special consideration since they have stimulated tremendous controversy over such basic concepts as density dependence and population regulation. A number of other theories covering particular aspects of population ecology have also been proposed and these are discussed here in less detail. Some theories have emphasized the factors causing fluctuations in populations, while others have concentrated on attempting to explain the apparent stability and the persistence of populations. As we shall see, the personal experience of the particular theorist usually determines the way in which he views the subject.

I. Nicholson's Theory

Nicholson's ideas on the determination of insect numbers were developed in a series of papers (Nicholson, 1933, 1954, 1957, 1958). His basic proposition is that populations are self-governing systems which exist in a state of balance with their environments, as a result of density-dependent opposition to population growth. Nicholson called those factors which respond to changes in population density in this way, density-governing factors. These intensify their opposition to population growth as numbers increase, eventually prevent further growth and then relax their opposition as numbers decrease. In more commonly used terminology these are density-dependent factors. The mechanism of density governance or regulation (cf. p. 12) Nicholson believed to be almost always intra-specific competition, either amongst the animals for a critically important requisite, or amongst natural enemies for which the animals concerned are requisites. Far from being a stationary state, he visualized balance as a state of oscillation about an equilibrium density, which continually changed with environmental conditions. He suggested that destructive factors do not always add to mortality since the intensity of competition will relax to make room for the destruction that they cause, thus resulting in a redistribution rather than an increase in mortality. Although population density can be regulated only by density-dependent factors, density-independent factors, or as Nicholson called them "non-reactive or density-legislative factors", have profound effects upon density, by influencing the level at which the population is regulated.

Nicholson's theory is certainly the most comprehensive and it is probably the most widely accepted theory that has been proposed. Its attraction to many ecologists lies I suspect in the idea of an evolved balance between animal populations and their environments. Many populations do appear to fluctuate little considering the huge potential powers of increase which some animals possess. On the other hand, there is little evidence from field populations that intra-specific competition and natural enemies can act in the way that Nicholson suggested (see Chapters 3 and 6). Competition for a resource can occur only at densities above that at which an animal's numbers start to affect the supply of the resource. Below this density it can play no part in regulation, and yet many populations exist at densities below this level for many generations (e.g. Klomp's population of *Bupalus*, p. 75). It is theoretically possible that natural enemies can act as density-dependent factors, at least over a limited range of densities, but the majority certainly do not act in this way (cf. Chapter 6). Field evidence as to the role of natural enemies is scant however, and density dependence is difficult to prove from field data. In my opinion, Nicholson's concept of regulation is unacceptable in the light of our present knowledge, but many ecologists would not agree with me.

II. Andrewartha and Birch's Theory

Andrewartha and Birch (1954) vigorously attacked Nicholson's ideas, on the grounds that there was no need to attach any special importance to density dependence. The division between density-dependent and density-independent they maintained to be imprecise, since the majority of mortality factors could be affected by density. For example, the proportion of a population surviving inclement weather, which is normally taken to be density-independent, might be greater in a small than in a large population, because there is only a limited number of places in the environment providing protection from the weather.

Andrewartha and Birch look at populations in a very different way to Nicholson. They consider that the numbers of animals are limited principally by the shortness of time when the rate of increase, r, is positive. Less frequently, they believe, populations are limited by the absolute or relative shortage of resources (see p. 23). Thus they reject the concept of stability and believe populations to be determined solely by the harshness of the environment.

Andrewartha and Birch's statement that population size is limited by the shortness of time during which the rate of increase is positive is something of a truism and it adds nothing to our understanding of the factors determining whether r is positive or negative. They are correct in maintaining that it is often difficult to classify the interactions between mortality and density, but to reject the concept of density dependence on these grounds results in the importance of these interactions being overlooked. In my opinion, however, Andrewartha and Birch did much to clarify the role of intra-specific competition by pointing out that populations of many animals are limited by resources being inaccessible relative to the animals' powers of searching. In such conditions, the supply of the resource is often independent of the number of animals searching for it and intra-specific competition is not occurring.

III. Milne's Theory

In many respects, Milne's ideas form a halfway house between the views of Nicholson and of Andrewartha and Birch (Milne 1957a, b, 1962). He believes that the latter underestimate the part played by density-related processes in the determination of animal numbers, but thinks that Nicholson overestimates the frequency with which intra-specific competition occurs in nature. He also maintains that natural enemies can never regulate the numbers of their prey, in the way that Nicholson proposes, since their effect is never perfectly density-dependent. Since the response of natural enemies to changes in prey numbers is rarely determined by prey density alone, and since the response may, in any case, be delayed, the action of natural enemies is always imperfectly density-dependent.

Milne's theory may be summarized as follows. For the most part, control of increase is due to the combined action of density-independent and imperfectly density-dependent environmental factors. In the comparatively rare cases where these fail, increase to the point of collective suicide is prevented by competition between individuals of the population. Decrease of numbers to zero is prevented ultimately by density-independent factors alone. For, unless the latter begin to favour increase instead of decrease, the remnant of the population must perish.

Thus Milne considers that intra-specific competition for resources is the only perfectly density-dependent factor, all other mortality factors being either density-independent or imperfectly density-dependent.

Milne's theory is based on a very different concept of population limitation to that proposed by Nicholson. He considers populations to be fluctuating within certain limits which are imposed by the environment. The upper limit is determined ultimately by the carrying capacity of the environment, while the lower limit is extinction. This is very different to the Nicholsonian concept of regulation, in which any change away from an equilibrium density is countered by a relaxation or an intensification of mortality. Many ecologists do not appreciate this distinction and speak of any density-dependent limitation of population size as regulation. This can be misleading, since some factors, such as intra-specific competition, can limit population growth but cannot regulate in the Nicholsonian sense, since they are not density-dependent at all densities.

IV. Other Theories

A number of other workers have proposed theories which emphasize particular aspects of population ecology.

Chitty's work on the population ecology of voles led him to publish a series of papers relating his findings to general theory (Chitty, 1960, 1965). Basically he believes that populations are numerically self-regulating, through genetically induced changes in the average vitality of individuals associated with changes in population density. In other words, weaker genotypes survive and multiply during the periods of favourable conditions when numbers rise. The average effect of any one environmental factor will then be greater at high densities than at low densities, due to the presence of these weaker genotypes. This, he maintains, will tend to stabilize the population, since mortality will be proportionally greater at population peaks than at troughs. As many workers have pointed out, genetic shifts of this sort cannot in themselves limit population growth. This will only occur when the environment becomes less favourable. While conditions allow population growth, numbers will rise irrespective of any genetic shift in the population. As we saw in Chapter 5, however, we know far too little about the inter-actions between population size and genetic make up.

Pimental (1961) applied evolutionary ideas to population ecology by proposing a genetic feed-back mechanism for the determination of numbers. The mechanism that he proposes is a feed-back system through selective pressures and genetic changes in interacting populations. For example, in a herbivore-plant system, increases in the herbivores, numbers will influence selection pressures on the plant population. This alters the genetic make-up of the plant population in terms of its average resistance to the herbivore, which in turn affects the herbivore popula-tion. The reactions of interacting populations of herbivore and plant, or predator and prey, will, he suggests, result in an evolved stability in their populations. Pimental does not suggest that this genetic feed-back mechanism is the only means of population control, but considers that it makes an important contribution to stability. The main objection to Pimental's theory is that there is invariably a multitude of selective forces acting on any one species, and it is unlikely that the selection pressure by, say, one species of herbivore on a plant will be great enough to ensure that this system works.

Wynne-Edwards (1962) suggested that many animals tend to limit their own numbers far below the carrying capacity of their habitats through the evolution of conventional goals of competition, such as territorial rights and social status, thus avoiding the harmful conse-quences of competition for real resources, such as food. We saw in Chapter 4 that there is very little evidence to suggest that territorial behaviour in itself limits population density, although intra-specific competition for territory may do so when densities are high. Similarly, social status normally does not prevent competition for food, but just ensures that the successful competitor gets enough for its needs. Added to this, in normal out-breeding populations, the evolution of conven-tional goals of competition can only be explained by invoking the con-cept of group selection. That is to say, one has to imagine that whole populations which are capable of maintaining their size below the carry-ing capacity of the habitat are at an advantage compared with those populations which cannot. For this to occur, some individuals within these populations, presumably low in the social hierarchy, must sometimes starve, or emigrate, or refrain from breeding even though there are enough resources available at the time. It is extremely difficult to see how this altruistic behaviour, which decreases the chance of survival and reproduction of the individual could have any selective advantage. In the light of our current understanding of the action of natural selection, Wynne-Edwards theory is therefore unacceptable.

The most recent contribution to population theory has come from den Boer (1968). He has suggested that the heterogeneity that is present in populations and in the habitats which they occupy tends to stabilize numbers and to reduce the chance of extinction. His argument follows the following lines. The effects of any one environmental factor will vary in different parts of the habitat, so that the effects of extreme conditions in one part of the habitat will be damped by the smaller effect of those conditions in other parts of the habitat. This will tend to lessen the chance of wide fluctuations in numbers in the entire population, especially if there is movement between the different sub-populations in the habitat. Different individuals (i.e. different genotypes) will differ in their susceptibility to any one environmental factor and this will also reduce the likelihood of wide fluctuations in numbers, and reduce the chance of extinction.

There is little doubt that heterogeneity does reduce the overall effect of violent fluctuations in the environment. We saw an example of this in the cinnabar moth on p. 74, in which heterogeneity in the timing of the larval stages, in their density and in the distribution of their food-plants reduced the overall effect of intra-specific competition for food and prevented extinction. There are many other examples of this sort (den Boer, 1968). The quantitative importance of heterogeneity, compared with that of density-dependent factors, in limiting population fluctuations is extremely difficult to assess. Clearly, it does play a part in limiting fluctuations, but, as we have seen, population growth is still ultimately limited by density-dependent competition in many populations.

V. Conclusions

We have seen that population theorists have proposed two basic ideas to account for the apparent stability of animal populations. Some, particularly those following Nicholson, consider that populations are regulated around an equilibrium density, so that the direction of population change at any one time is determined largely by the size of the population in relation to this equilibrium. The second school of thought (e.g. Milne) believes that populations simply fluctuate between certain limits. The upper limit is determined by the carrying capacity of the habitat and the lower limit is extinction. Within these limits, population change is usually at random with respect to population size.

In my opinion, the first of these two concepts can be rejected on the grounds that no factor has been demonstrated to act in a way that would bring about population regulation. For this to happen, opposition to population growth must be density-dependent at all densities. Nicholson suggests that competition will act in this way, but competition for resources can cause density-dependent limitation only at high densities. Below the density where population size is affecting the supply of a resource, intra-specific competition will not occur. It is theoretically possible for natural enemies to regulate the numbers of their prey, if their aggregate behavioural response to changes in prey density is large (see p. 46). To my knowledge however, none has been demonstrated to be capable of acting in this way in the field. In those cases where density dependence has been demonstrated, the slope of the regression of mortality on density has been too small to regulate a population in a rapidly changing environment.

The second concept of population limitation appears to be far more realistic. Populations have frequently been demonstrated to be limited by intra-specific competition for resources, and extinction of local populations is not abnormal, particularly at the edge of the distribution of species. Intra-specific competition is difficult to identify in the field unless it results in a heavy mortality. Added to this its effect varies with different types of resource; for example, competition for food may result in violent fluctuations in number, whilst competition for less essential resources, such as breeding territory, results in very little fluctuation in population size. The effect of competition will also depend upon whether the interaction between individuals is of a scramble- or contest-type.

There has been considerable discussion amongst ecologists as to the frequency with which intra-specific competition occurs in animal populations. Competition is not always easy to identify and its effects are often transient, since many animals tend to disperse in response to overcrowding. In my opinion, many ecologists underestimate how commonly intra-specific competition limits population growth in many species. Having said this, there is equally no doubt that many populations can exist for long periods without competition occurring. We saw several examples in Chapters 8 and 9 of populations which rarely, if ever, reached a size where competition for resources occur, although other populations of the same species regularly did so (e.g. cinnabar moth, p. 74; pine looper, p. 79; larch tortrix, p. 111). Whether or not those populations which rarely reach a size where competition occurs

F

are limited by density-dependent processes in uncertain, but it seems unlikely. As we saw in Chapter 8, it is more likely that the growth of these populations is limited by the harshness of an array of density-independent factors, as Milne suggests in his theory.

We are still a long way from having a completely acceptable generalized theory to explain animal numbers. This is perhaps not surprising when one appreciates the extremely complex interactions of the environmental factors affecting population size. Until we have a more solid basis of field data on which to build, it is pointless to be dogmatic in following one or other of the alternative theories which have been proposed. At present the subject requires an open mind.

11. Applications of Population Ecology

Population ecology is of potential economic importance whenever Man endeavours to control animal populations. There are two broad fields where this applies; first the control of pests and secondly, the conservation of food animals and wildlife. In this chapter we shall be looking at the ways in which population ecology can be applied and the ways in which these applications can add to our knowledge of populations.

I. Pest Species

Any animal which does economic damage to crops and domesticated animals, or is harmful to human health, constitutes a pest. Generally, pests have to be abundant, at least at certain times, in order to do economic damage. There are exceptions to this however, and some species, particularly those carrying disease, can do considerable harm at very low densities. An example of this is the tsetse fly which transmits trypanosomiasis to cattle and Man. However, as a general rule, a species needs to be abundant to be a pest.

As we have seen, many factors determine the abundance of animals, but some generalizations can be made about what makes some species pests. Frequently pests are man-made (Uvarov, 1964) in that they are species which occur in low numbers in wild habitats but increase enormously in number in more favourable conditions created by Man. The creation of pests can stem from three main causes. By far the commonest cause is Man providing the species with a better supply of some limiting resource. Commonly it is the pests' food supply which is improved by Man growing crops in large areas of monoculture, thus providing an almost unlimited food supply. Other resources besides food may be affected by Man's actions. For example, outbreaks of the Moroccan locust originate only from grasslands which are heavily overgrazed by sheep (Dempster, 1957). This locust requires bare, well trampled soil in which to lay its eggs and overgrazing provides this.

The second way in which Man may create pests is by making crops unsuitable for natural enemies which may limit the pests numbers in natural habitats. We shall see examples of this when we look at the effects of chemical control on pest populations.

Lastly, Man may introduce a species into a new region, where it may multiply to pest proportions in the absence of its natural enemies. In the case of vertebrate pests, such as the rabbit and grey squirrel, Man has often introduced the species intentionally. Amongst the invertebrates however, pest species have usually been introduced unintentionally, often with introduced plants.

A. Chemical Pest Control

Chemical control of pests has resulted in enormous benefits in terms of increased food supply and the reduction of disease. On the other hand, some pests are inadequately controlled by chemical means and the use of pesticides has created many new problems.

Virtually all pesticides are non-specific poisons. That is to say they are poisonous to a wide range of different organisms. Because of this, the precise effect that a pesticide has when sprayed onto a crop may be extremely complex (see Dempster, 1974). Because of the interdependence of different species inhabiting any crop, it is impossible to predict the detailed effects of any one pesticide. The effects depend upon the relative sensitivity of the different interacting species to the chemical.

Control brought about by pesticide applications is sometimes disappointing, since pests often recur surprisingly quickly. Also there are many cases where the pest population has then built up to far greater numbers than occurred before spraying. This is known as "pest resurgence". Added to this, new pests have often arisen after spraying; that is, species which had previously been causing little or no damage to the crop. The main cause of pest resurgence and the creation of new pests is that the pesticide kills many of the natural enemies and competitors which were previously reducing the pest's numbers.

An example of pest resurgence can be seen with the control of the small cabbage white butterfly (*Pieris rapae*) with DDT (Dempster, 1968b). This butterfly is a pest of brassica crops, such as cabbage, cauliflowers and Brussels sprouts, and until recently it was normally controlled with DDT. This gives a good control of the caterpillars of *Pieris*; when applied correctly it will kill virtually 100% of the caterpillars present on the crop at the time of spraying. Control is short lived, however, because as the plants grow during the summer, new leaves are produced which are free from the insecticide. The adult butterfly lays its eggs on these newly expanded leaves of the plant and the caterpillars feed on these and within the heart of the plant. Figure 48

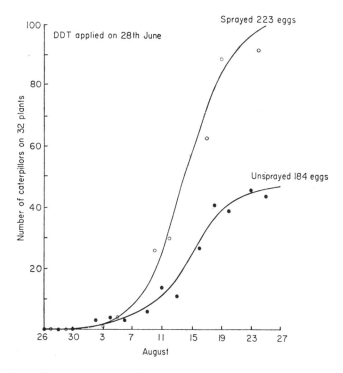

Fig. 48: The build up in numbers of *Pieris rapae* caterpillars on sprayed and unsprayed plots.

shows the build up of the second generation of *Pieris* on sprayed and unsprayed plots, and it will be seen that although similar numbers of eggs were laid on the two plots, the number of caterpillars increased far more rapidly on the sprayed area. The reason for this is that the DDT had killed many of the arthropod predators of the pest. These normally take 50–70% of the young caterpillars on an unsprayed crop (Dempster,

1967). By far the most important of these are ground-living species which climb the plants at night and feed on the caterpillars. The ground-beetle, *Harpalus rufipes* is particularly important as a predator of *Pieris*. Although DDT is put on as a foliage application, much of it finishes up in the surface layers of the soil and here it is extremely persistent. This means that its effect on the ground-living predators lasts long after its effect on the pest is lost, and this results in resurgence of the pest.

The effect of DDT on the predators of *Pieris* and the resultant resurgence of the pest clearly demonstrates the impact that these have in unsprayed areas. On the other hand, they do not prevent *Pieris* reaching pest status on unsprayed crops in some years. There are however, examples of species which were previously causing no economic damage, increasing to pest status as a result of pesticides eliminating their natural enemies. One of the best documented examples of this is the fruit tree red spider mite, *Panonychus ulmi*. This species was at one time of no economic importance and even today its numbers are low in orchards not treated with pesticides, owing to a wide range of natural enemies which feed on it (Collyer, 1953).

Panonychus ulmi was virtually unknown in British orchards before about 1925. Since then, however, it has gradually built up in importance until now it is one of our most serious apple pests. The use of sulphur sprays in orchards led to heavy infestations of the mite, but it was not until the introduction of DDT in the early 1950s to control codling moth that huge outbreaks of the mite occurred. The detailed effects of this chemical are complicated; it kills many of the predators of the mite and other phytophagous mites, such as *Bryobia*, which may be competing with *Panonychus*. There is also some evidence which suggests that DDT increases the fecundity of the mite by changing the nutritive status of the host plants (Hueck *et al.*, 1952). Fertilizer treatments also affect the mite's numbers, since high nitrogen content of the leaves leads to high mite populations. Just how important changes in the reproduction of *Panonychus* are in determining population size is uncertain, without detailed population data for the species.

It will be seen that the overall effects of one pesticide on an animal's population may be extremely complicated. We are still a long way from understanding the intricacies of this for any one chemical and species. This knowledge can be obtained only by knowing more about the population ecology of each pest. Only then can we hope to reap the benefits of chemical control methods without harmful repercussions. There has been a growing awareness of this amongst economic entomologists during the past ten years and a more comprehensive approach to the control of insect pests is developing. This has led to the idea of integrated control, in which attempts are made to integrate pesticides into the existing framework of natural control agencies. By the use of more specific pesticides, timed to do least harm to non-target species, especially the pest's natural enemies, the more harmful side-effects of chemical control may be reduced.

B. Biological Control of Pests

Pesticides are not the only means of combating pests; some species have been successfully controlled by biological means. We saw examples of this on pp. 42–43, with the biological control of cottony-cushion scale in California and of rabbits in Britain. In these and in many other examples of successful biological control, an introduced pest has been brought under control by the introduction of a natural enemy from its country of origin. Predators, parasites and pathogens have all been used in this way to control introduced animal pests, while herbivores and pathogens have been used against weeds.

There is scarcely a country whose flora and fauna has not been affected by Man's introductions. Oceanic islands, such as Hawaii and New Zealand, have suffered particularly in this respect. About sixty exotic mammals and birds have been introduced to and are now well established in New Zeland alone (Elton, 1958). Once they have become established, many introduced species have multiplied and spread enormously in the absence of the natural curbs to population growth which exist in their native lands. Some of our worst agricultural pests have originated in this way.

Many attempts at establishing natural enemies of introduced pest species have failed, due to their failure to tolerate their new environment. Other species have become established, but have failed to bring about control of the pest. The reasons for such failures are almost always unknown because of insufficient study of the population ecology of the species concerned. Often the cheapest and quickest way of finding out whether a species is capable of controlling a pest's numbers below an economic level is to try it and see, and this has frequently been the approach of biological control workers. However, much time and labour may be avoided by a prior knowledge of the ways in which the enemy and pest populations interact. An example of this can be seen from the attempts at the biological control of the weed, *Senecio jacobaea* (ragwort), by the cinnabar moth (*Tyria jacobaeae*).

Senecio jacobaea is a native of Europe, but it has become established in many other parts of the World, such as Australia, New Zealand, the United States, and Canada. Here it has become an important weed of pastures, since when eaten it causes cirrhosis of the liver in cattle and horses. Cinnabar moth was an obvious candidate for the biological control of ragwort, because of the spectacular defoliation caused by its caterpillars in some localities. Since Cameron's pioneer work (Cameron, 1935), there have been many attempts to control ragwort by introducing the moth, but with very limited success (Bornemissza, 1966; Frick and Holloway, 1964; Hawkes, 1968; Wilkinson, 1965). The population study of the cinnabar moth described on pp. 63–75, gives some indications as to why failure in control may occur.

Three interacting factors appear to be particularly important in determining the effect of the moth on ragwort, namely climate, soil and grazing pressure. At Weeting Heath, rainfall is low, the soil is well drained and infertile, and the vegetation is overgrazed by rabbits. Here the moth can build up to numbers where it regularly defoliates the plant. The ragwort plants are small and there is practically no regrowth from the crown of the plant after defoliation. There is, however, considerable regeneration from root-buds and in some years this may lead to an increase in the plant population. In 1968 the number of ragwort plants increased from 5 to $68/m^2$ as a result of regeneration following defoliation. This increase may have been abnormal since the autumn of 1968 was exceptionally wet, but it demonstrates the enormous powers of regeneration of the plant under some environmental conditions. It also shows that the action of the moth can lead to an increase in the number of plants under these circumstances.

Small plants of ragwort, whether resulting from seed or from root buds, do not compete well with grasses (Harper and Wood, 1957), and regeneration of the plants at Weeting was largely a result of the over-grazed condition of the vegetation. Heavy grazing also affects the survival of the moth, because fewer arthropod predators live in the shorter, sparser vegetation (Dempster, 1971).

On more fertile soils, the plants will regenerate mainly by regrowth from their crowns. Defoliation will result in fewer seeds being produced, but it may take several years of defoliation to kill the plants. Harris (1973) describes a situation like this in British Columbia, where the moth has defoliated the plants for four successive years with little effect on the number of plants.

If conditions do not favour excessive regeneration, the moth can reduce the numbers of plants. This happened in 1967 and 1971 at Weeting (see Table XI, p. 69). Similarly, Harris (1973) found that the late springs in Nova Scotia, resulted in defoliation by cinnabar moth occurring late in the summer. There was then too little time for the plants to regenerate before the winter set in.

Lastly, the population study of the moth showed that it is incapable of reaching numbers where it defoliates the plant on areas of poorly drained soil, because of high mortality in the pupal stage (see p. 74). Also, ragwort is able to occupy some habitats where the moth is unable to survive because of excessive wetness.

There is clearly then a very limited set of circumstances under which the moth can control the numbers of ragwort. For successful biological control the soil must be well drained; the climate must restrict regeneration and overgrazing must be controlled. It is therefore not surprising that attempts at controlling ragwort with this moth have been so unsuccessful.

Studies of this sort show how complex are the interactions between any two species. Without a detailed knowledge of this sort, biological control will always be a very hit or miss affair.

The classical examples of biological control have all involved the introduction of a natural enemy of some previously introduced pest species. Natural enemies are however, also of potential value in limiting the numbers of some endemic pests. There is growing interest among applied biologists in attempting to boost the impact of native enemies of pests by manipulation of the crop environment. This approach is particularly valuable as a basis for integrated control, in which chemical and biological methods of pest control are integrated as far as possible (see p. 133). Often quite small changes in the way in which a crop is grown can have a large impact upon pests and their enemies. There are obviously limitations to what can be done in altering the way in which crops are grown, set by the economics of cultivation and harvesting, but this approach to pest control has I believe much to offer (Dempster and Coaker, 1974; Doutt and Nakata, 1965).

II. Predation by Man

Although Man is primarily dependent upon agriculture and domesticated animals for protein, most human communities also exploit natural populations of fish, game animals or birds. Many species, such as the passenger pigeon (*Ectopistes migratorius*) have been over-exploited by Man in the past, and clearly any rational use of these resources demands a knowledge of the population ecology of the species concerned. Some animal populations (e.g. some marine fish) are extremely resilient and appear to be able to withstand extremely high rates of predation by Man. Others are far more vulnerable (e.g. whales) and are in danger of extinction through Man's activities. The reasons for this become apparent when we look at their population dynamics.

A. Fish Populations

Fishery biologists have led the way in attempts at assessing the level of predation which wild populations can withstand. As with most exploited animals, it is mainly a particular age- or size-class which is taken and in some species the mortality caused by fishing may be considerable. For example, about 50% of the larger plaice (*Pleuronectes platessa*) are caught each year in the North Sea, compared with a natural mortality in this age-class of only 10–15% (Beverton, 1962). Although fish stocks have proved extremely resistant to exploitation, the impact of fishing can

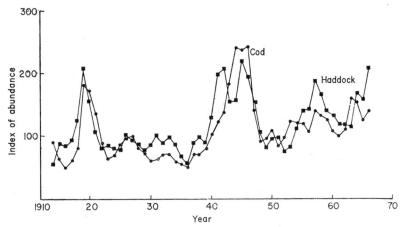

Fig. 49: Variations in the abundance of haddock and cod in the North Sea.

easily be seen by the recovery which occurs as soon as Man's activities are reduced. Figure 49 shows indices of abundance of cod (*Gadus morrhua*) and haddock (*Melanogrammus aeglefinus*), estimated from the catch per unit fishing time by British trawlers between 1914–67 (Gulland, 1971). It can be seen that the abundance of these fish increased markedly after the wars of 1914–18 and 1939–45, when fishing pressure was reduced. This demonstrates the effect of fishing in reducing the average level of these fish populations. In this, Man is having a similar effect to that seen when natural predators are used in biological control (see for example, the impact of *Rhodolia* on *Icerya*, p. 42).

There is very little variation in the abundance of many exploited fish (see Fig. 49) and this has led to the idea amongst many ecologists that fish populations present very good evidence of population regulation. This is, however, a false impression since data such as those in Fig. 49 include individuals of many different age classes. These species have a natural life span of at least 10 years, up to 30 years in some cases, and although the total population changes little, recruitment to a fishable age may fluctuate widely from year to year. Recruitment in the North Sea haddock varies over a range of 500-fold (Parrish, 1956), although total catches vary by only about four-fold.

Although fish biologists have long series of data on the numbers of different age-classes caught by fishermen, very little is known about natural mortality, particularly of the very young stages, before they become a fishable size. Many fish lay enormous numbers of eggs and there is an extremely high mortality during early life.

One of the best studied, exploited fish is the plaice (*Pleuronectes platessa*). Catches of this species have fluctuated little over the past fifty years, but the reasons for this apparent stability are far from certain (Beverton, 1962).

This species is not caught before it is 3–4 years old and it becomes mature about one year later. Data for numbers caught refer to mainly adult fish. As we saw with the cod and haddock, there was an increase in the number of plaice caught immediately after the last war. When fishing restarted in 1945 the population was probably five or six times higher than during the 1930s. Growth of the older fish during the war period was retarded somewhat, so that adult fish weighed 15–20% less than pre-war fish of the same age. This suggests that there was intra-specific competition for food occurring with the increased number of adult fish. This will have had no effect upon survival, but it will have reduced the fecundity of females at any given age, since fecundity is dependent upon body weight. Beverton showed however, that recruitment to the fishable age-classes was not dependent upon the size of the existing adult population, so that variations in fecundity with increases in density probably had little effect on this recruitment. Recruitment to adult did in fact vary little during 26 years for which data were available, only in the order of six-fold. This is particularly surprising in view of the enormous fecundity of this species (up to one million eggs per female).

North Sea plaice spawn mainly in two restricted areas, in the Heligoland Bight and in the southern North Sea. In years of high adult density there appears to have been no spread of spawning into less favourable areas. Instead, there was an increase in the density of eggs within the restricted spawning areas.

Mortality is exceedingly high in the egg stage and in the first few weeks after hatching (Harding and Talbot, 1973). In contrast to many other marine fish, cannibalism has not been recorded in plaice, but many predators probably feed on the eggs and larvae. The action of these is unlikely to be density-dependent however. Beverton suggests that intra-specific competition for food may well limit larval populations. Larval mortality has been shown to be related to food supply in a number of other fish species (Beverton and Holt, 1957), and since plaice larvae are very specific feeders on the tunicate, *Oikopleura*, food shortage may well be important at this time. *Oikopleura* is very patchily distributed and plaice larvae have been shown to be in poor condition at times of low abundance of this prey. Besides the direct effects of starvation, starving plaice larvae may be more susceptible to adverse physical conditions. In any case, because food shortage will prolong larval development, it is likely to increase mortality, since the larval stage is so much more susceptible than older stages. Beverton suggests that catastrophic mortality from starvation may be prevented by the heterogeneity in the distribution of plaice and *Oikopleura* and by the heterogeneity in the development of plaice larvae, older larvae surviving competition better than young ones.

Although data are not available to prove this, it seems likely that intra-specific competition for food limits the recruitment of plaice into the adult age-classes. The subsequent, apparent stability in population size probably reflects a very stable fishing pressure against this species which keeps the population below that where competition occurs between adult fish. If this is so, the dynamics of this plaice population has many similarities to the exploited population of the edible cockle described on pp. 86–92. The main difference between the two is that the cockle larvae are competing with other age classes, including adults, for space. Adult and larval plaice do not compete because the larvae are pelagic whereas the adults are demersal. In the edible cockle, competition leads to over-compensation, since space left as a result of high adult mortality can be occupied by very large numbers of young cockles (as in 1963, p. 86). As these grow, overcrowding occurs and subsequent settlement of larvae is restricted, thus leading to violent oscillations in recruitment.

The intra-specific competition for space which we saw in the edible cockle, appears to be important in other shell fish also. Korringa (1971) described a very similar case in the oyster, *Ostrea edulis*. The natural oyster beds in the Ooster Schelde, Netherlands, produced year after year between a half and three quarters of a million marketable oysters. The limiting factor was apparently the scarcity of suitable material on which the larvae could settle, since when more suitable substrate was supplied, the oyster population grew until 25–30 million oysters were harvested each year from the same area. Efforts to increase the stock still further failed because food then became a limiting factor and this led to poor growth.

B. Marine Mammal Populations

In contrast to fish population, those of the marine mammals are particularly susceptible to over-exploitation. This can be seen from the history of whaling (Gulland, 1971).

The first commercial whale fisheries hunted right whales (*Balaena mysticetus* and *Eubalaena glacialis*) in the Atlantic at the beginning of the nineteenth century. Whaling quickly rose to being an important industry, with several hundred vessels fishing from Britain and Holland.

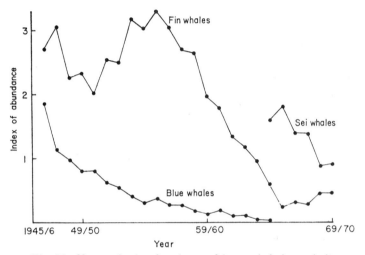

Fig. 50: Changes in the abundance of Antarctic baleen whales.

By midway through that century however, only a handful of boats were still in operation. The Atlantic right whales had become almost extinct, and they remain extremely rare to this day. The next big whaling venture came from the U.S.A.; this time on the sperm whales (*Physeter catodon*) in the Pacific. Although this species was reduced by hunting, the market for whale oil dropped with the discovery of petroleum, before its numbers became seriously lowered. With the invention of the harpoon gun, Man could go after bigger whales and so the last great era of whaling began some 50 years ago in the Antarctic. The blue whale (*Balaenoptera musculus*) and fin whale (*Balaenoptera physalus*) were the most important species hunted. By 1946 there was sufficient alarm at the drop in catches that the International Whaling Commission was set up and a quota was imposed on the numbers which could be taken. This failed to stop the decline in the blue whale (Fig. 50) and there was then introduced a complete ban on the taking of this species and the humpback whale (*Megaptera novaeangliae*). By the early 1960s, the fin whale became scarce and whalers then turned to sei (*Balaenoptera borealis*) and sperm whales. In 1966–67 the quota of whales allowed was reduced still further. This time the quota was based upon the estimated sustainable yield of fin and sei whales and there are signs that this has led to a levelling out of the downward trend of the populations. The maximum sustainable yield of the population may be calculated from a number of mathematical models. It may be taken as equal to the innate rate of increase of the species (see p. 5), or in the logistic model it is $K/2$ (see p. 6). At present, however, the population parameters from which it can be calculated are inadequately known. In particular, very little is known about the natural mortality of whales. It remains to be seen whether the quota which has been imposed will allow stocks of these species to recover.

There have been some interesting changes in the rates of reproduction of some species of whale in response to over-exploitation by Man. There is evidence for the fin whale that there has been an increase in the pregnancy rate and a decrease in the age at maturation in recent years (Laws, 1962). This may be the result of the heavy selection pressures caused by Man tending to take a high proportion of the older whales. It seems likely that natural selection has caused a shift in the mean age of maturation because those individuals which mature earliest have tended to leave more offspring.

The story of Man's short-sighted greed which has led to the near extinction of so many whale species is not unique. Many other large vertebrates have gone the same way. The main difference between the mammals (whales) and fish populations is that mammals have a far lower fecundity. For example, the female plaice lays about a million eggs, whereas fin whales produce one young every two years. Whales are therefore less able to withstand the added high mortality caused by Man's predation.

III. Nature Conservation

The previous section deals with one aspect of Nature Conservation, namely, the conservation of species useful to Man for food, or some other natural resource. In recent years however, there has been an increasing awareness of the need for conservation of wildlife and of wild places for recreational and scientific reasons. It is the natural course of events for species to become extinct, but Man is speeding up the processes of change to such an extent that a large part of our wildlife heritage will be lost unless positive action is taken to protect it.

It is one thing to wish to conserve a particular animal, but it is quite another to know how to set about it. First one needs to discover why the species is in danger of extinction. Sometimes the cause is man-made, such as direct persecution, habitat destruction, or pollution, but equally it may be a natural cause. Only by understanding the requirements of the species and the factors determining its abundance can we be certain of the cause of any population decline. Clearly then, this is basically a question of its population ecology.

Throughout this book we have seen that natural populations are determined by a complex of interacting factors. Frequently, populations are permanently kept below the carrying capacity of their habitats by the impact of environmental factors, such as natural enemies, competing species, or climate. If the environment is improved, the population will rise until it is ultimately limited by shortage of resources.

There are many examples of species which, following protection by Man, have then built up into such large numbers that food becomes a limiting resource. A good example is to be found in some of the large African herbivores. Man has hunted many of these for a long time, both for meat and to protect his crops. At the same time Man has killed many of the larger predators which were preying on these herbivores. Subsequent protection in game parks has led to their populations increasing to such an extent that they have done enormous damage to the vegetation in the reserves. It has now proved necessary to control the population size of many species in order to conserve them.

This situation exemplifies once more that the removal of one constraint to population growth will simply allow numbers to increase until some other constraint is invoked. Ultimately, it will be intra-specific competition which prevents further growth. The absolute density at which this occurs will vary from animal to animal and habitat to habitat. The carrying capacity of many heterogeneous natural habitats will be low for many species, and this certainly accounts for the rareness of some animals. It is only by studying the habitat requirements of a species that the limiting resource can be identified. In general, the more complex the life cycle of the animal, the more complex are its requirements, and the more likely are its numbers to be limited by a resource which is required at some stage in its development.

The majority of animal species occur in very low numbers, yet most population studies have been on more abundant species. We are urgently in need of more knowledge of the population ecology of rare species. Perhaps the demands of conservation will cause more ecologists to look at these, in the same way as pest control has stimulated the study of more abundant species in the past.

IV. Man

Although Man now controls much of his own environment, his numbers are still determined by a similar array of factors as affect populations of other animals.

Man has greatly increased the carrying capacity of the environment in which he lives by the growing of crops and by the domestication of animals. The supply of food however, still undergoes frequent fluctuations due to weather and other animals. Famines often result from the failure of crops, from bad weather or from pests (i.e. inter-specific competition). Other resources besides food may limit population size and intra-specific competition occurs when resources become scarce. In Man, warfare, ritual sacrifice, and infanticide are forms of mutual interference.

Although predators are now no longer of any importance to Man, disease can have an enormous influence on Man's abundance. Here again however, Man is gradually overcoming this as a major mortality factor.

It is impossible to obtain reliable estimates of population size further back then about 100 years, but the trend in Man's numbers appears to be almost exponential (Ehrlich and Ehrlich, 1970). Over the past 100 years the population has doubled, and the rate of growth is increasing. This is due primarily to the greatly improved survival of Man as a result of his success at combating disease and famine.

In some parts of the World, birth-rates are beginning to decline but at far too slow a rate to counter the improved survival. Obviously, for stability, birth-rates must balance death-rates. At present the death-rate in more developed countries is approaching 1.0% per year. For stability the birth-rate must be reduced to the same level.

Economic, social and psychological factors all play a part in determining Man's numbers, but the basic principles of population ecology still apply to him. There is an upper limit to the carrying capacity of the World and Man is rapidly approaching this. When this is reached intra-specific competition, with all of its horrible side effects, will bring the population down again. Fortunately, sufficient people are now aware of this problem to give one hope that we may yet solve it by controlling birth-rates.

References

Anderson, N. H. (1962). Growth and fecundity of *Anthocoris* spp reared on various prey (Heteroptera: Anthocoridae). *Entomologia exp. appl.* **5,** 40–52.

Andrewartha, H. G. and Birch, L. C. (1954). "The Distribution and Abundance of Animals". University Chicago Press, Chicago.

Baker, R. R. (1972). Territorial behaviour of the nymphalid butterflies, *Aglais urticae* (L) and *Inarchis io* (L). *J. Anim. Ecol.* **41,** 453–469.

Bakker, K. (1961). An analysis of factors which determine success in competition for food among larvae of *Drosophila melanogaster*. *Archs néerl. Zool.* **14,** 200–281.

Bakker, K. (1964). Backgrounds of controversies about population theories and their terminologies. *Z. angew. Ent.* **53,** 187–208.

Baltensweiler, W. (1968). The cyclic population dynamics of the grey larch tortrix, *Zeiraphera griseana* Hübner (= *Semasia diniana* Guenée) (Lepidoptera: Tortricidae). *In* "Insect Abundance" (T. R. E. Southwood, ed.) pp. 88–97. Blackwell Scientific Publications, Oxford.

Benson, J. F. (1973a). Some problems of testing for density-dependence in animal populations. *Oecologia* **13,** 183–190.

Benson, J. F. (1973b). The biology of Lepidoptera infesting stored products, with special reference to population dynamics. *Biol. Rev.* **48,** 1–26.

Benson, J. F. (1973c). Intraspecific competition in the population dynamics of *Bracon hebetor* Say. (Hymenoptera, Braconidae). *J. Anim. Ecol.* **42,** 105–124.

Bess, H. A. (1961). Population ecology of the Gypsy Moth, *Pothetria dispar* L. (Lepidoptera: Lymantridae). *Bull. Conn. agric. Exp. Stn.* **646,** 4–43.

Bevan, D. (1966). Pine Looper Moth, *Bupalus piniarius. Leafl. For. Commn.* No. 32, pp. 12.

Beverton, R. J. H. (1962). Long-term dynamics of certain North Sea fish populations. *In* "The Exploitation of Natural Animal Populations" (E. D. LeCren and M. W. Holdgate, eds.), pp. 242–259. Blackwell Scientific Publications, Oxford.

Beverton, R. J. H. and Holt, S. J. (1957). On the dynamics of exploited fish populations. *Fishery Invest., Lond.,* Ser. II. **19,** 1–533.

Birch, L. C. (1953). Experimental background to the study of the distribution and abundance of insects. III. The relation between innate capacity for increase and survival of different species of beetles living together on the same food. *Evolution,* Lancaster, **7,** 136–144.

Birch, L. C. (1957). The meanings of competition. *Am. Nat.* **91,** 5–18.

Blair, W. F. (1957). Changes in vertebrate populations under conditions of drought. *Cold Spring Harb. Symp. quant. Biol.* **22,** 273–275.

Blank, T. H., Southwood, T. R. E. and Cross, D. J. (1967). The ecology of the partridge. I. Outline of the population processes, with particular reference to chick mortality and nest density. *J. Anim. Ecol.* **36,** 549–556.

Bornemissza, G. F. (1966). An attempt to control ragwort in Australia with the cinnabar moth. *Aust. J. Zool.* **14,** 201–243.

Brown, J. L. (1969). Territorial behaviour and population regulation in birds. *Wilson Bull.* **81,** 293–329.

Browning, T. O. (1968). "Animal Populations". Hutchinson, London.

Burnett, T. (1951). Effects of temperature and host density on the rate of increase of an insect parasite. *Am. Nat.* **85,** 337–352.

Burnett, T. (1958). Dispersal of an insect parasite over a small plot. *Can. Ent.* **90,** 279–283.

Cameron, E. (1935). A study of the natural control of ragwort (*Senecio jacobaea* L.). *J. Ecol.* **23,** 265–322.

Chandler, A. E. F. (1968). The relationship between aphid infestations and oviposition by aphidophagous Syrphidae (Diptera). *Ann. appl. Biol.* **61,** 425–434.

Chitty, D. (1952). Mortality among voles (*Microtus agrestis*) at Lake Vyrnwy, Montgomeryshire in 1936–9. *Phil. Trans. R. Soc.*, Ser. B, **236,** 505–552.

Chitty, D. (1957). Self regulation of numbers through changes in viability. *Cold Spring Harb. Symp. quant. Biol.* **22,** 277–280.

Chitty, D. (1960). Population processes in the vole and their relevance to general theory. *Can. J. Zool.* **38,** 99–113.

Chitty, D. (1965). Predicting qualitative changes in insect populations. *Int. Congr. Ent.*, 12. London, 1964, 384–386.

Clark, L. R., Geier, P. W., Hughes, R. D. and Morris, R. F. (1967). "The Ecology of Insect Populations in Theory and Practice". Methuen, London.

Collyer, E. (1953). Insect population balance and chemical control of pests. *Chemy Ind.*, 1044–1046.

Crisp, D. J. (1964). The effects of the severe winter of 1962–63 on marine life in Britain. *J. Anim. Ecol.* **33,** 165–210.

Crissey, W. F. and Darrow, R. W. (1949). A study of predator control on Valcour Island. *N.Y. State Conserv. Dept., Division of Fish and Game, Res. Ser.* No. 1, 1–28.

Crombie, A. C. (1945). On competition between different species of graminivorous insects. *Proc. R. ent. Soc.*, Ser. B, **132,** 362–395.

D'Ancona, U. (1954). The struggle for existence. *Biblthca biotheor.* **6,** 1–274.

de Bach, P. and Smith, H. S. (1941). The effect of host density on the rate of reproduction of entomophagous parasites. *J. econ. Ent.* **34,** 741–745.

Deevey, E. S. (1947). Life tables for natural populations of animals. *Q. Rev. Biol.* **22,** 283–314.

Dempster, J. P. (1957). The population dynamics of the Moroccan Locust (*Dociostaurus maroccanus* Thunberg) in Cyprus. *Anti-Locust Bull.* **27,** 1–60.

Dempster, J. P. (1960). A quantitative study of the predators on the eggs and larvae of the broom beetle, *Phytodecta olivacea* Forster, using the precipitin test. *J. Anim. Ecol.* **29,** 149–167.

Dempster, J. P. (1963a). The natural prey of three species of *Anthocoris* (Heteroptera: Anthocoridae) living on broom (*Sarothamnus scoparius* L.). *Entomologia exp. appl.* **6,** 149–155.

Dempster, J. P. (1963b). The population dynamics of grasshoppers and locusts. *Biol. Rev.* **38,** 490–529.

Dempster, J. P. (1967). The control of *Pieris rapae* with DDT. I. The natural mortality of the young stages of *Pieris. J. appl. Ecol.* **4,** 485–500.

Dempster, J. P. (1968a). Intra-specific competition and dispersal: as exemplified by a psyllid and its anthocorid predator. *In* "Insect Abundance" (T. R. E. Southwood, ed.) pp. 8–17. Blackwell Scientific Publications, Oxford.

Dempster, J. P. (1968b). The control of *Pieris rapae* with DDT. II. Survival of the young stages of *Pieris* after spraying. *J. appl. Ecol.* **5,** 451–462.

Dempster, J. P. (1971). The population ecology of the cinnabar moth, *Tyria jacobaeae* L. (Lepidoptera: Arctiidae). *Oecologia* **7,** 26–67

Dempster, J. P. (1974). Effects of organochlorine insecticides on animal populations. *In* "Organochlorine Insecticides: Persistent Organic Pollutants." (F. Moriarty, ed.), pp. 231–248. Academic Press, London.

Dempster, J. P. and Coaker, T. H. (1974). Diversification of crop ecosystems as a means of controlling pests. *In* "Biology in Pest and Disease Control" (D. Price Jones and M. E. Solomon, eds.), pp. 106–114. Blackwell Scientific Publications, Oxford.

Dempster, J. P., Richards, O. W. and Waloff, N. (1959). Carabidae as predators of the pupal stage of the chrysomelid beetle, *Phytodecta olivacea* (Forster). *Oikos* **10,** 65–70.

den Boer, P. J. (1968). Spreading of risk and stabilization of animal numbers. *Acta biotheor.* **18,** 165–194.

De Vore, I. and Hall, K. R. L. (1975). Baboon ecology. *In* "Primate Behaviour, Field Studies of Monkeys and Apes" (I. De Vore, ed.), pp. 20–52. Holt, Rinehart and Wilson, New York.

Dixon, A. F. G. and Russel, R. J. (1972). The effectiveness of *Anthocoris nemorum* and *A. confusus* (Hemiptera: Anthocoridae) as predators of the Sycamore Aphid, *Drepanosiphum platanoides.* II. Searching behaviour and the incidence of predation in the field. *Entomolgia exp. appl.* **15,** 35–50.

Doutt, R. L. and Nakata, J. (1965). Parasites for control of grape leafhopper. *Calif. Agric.* **19,** 3.

Ehrlich, P. R., Breedlove, D. E., Brussard, P. F. and Sharp, M. A. (1972). Weather and the "regulation" of subalpine populations. *Ecology* **53,** 243–247.

Ehrlich, P. R. and Ehrlich, A. H. (1970). "Population, Resources, Environment". Freeman, San Francisco.

Elton, C. (1927). "Animal Ecology", Sidgwick & Jackson, London.

Elton, C. (1942). "Voles, Mice and Lemmings", Clarendon Press, Oxford.

Elton, C. (1958). "The Ecology of Invasions by Animals", Methuen, London.

Elton, C. and Nicholson, M. (1942). Fluctuations in numbers of muskrat (*Ondatra zibethica*) in Canada. *J. Anim. Ecol.* **11,** 96–126.

Embree, D. G. (1966). The role of introduced parasites in the control of the winter moth in Nova Scotia. *Can. Ent.* **98**, 1159–1168.

Frick, K. E. and Holloway, J. K. (1964). Establishment of the Cinnabar Moth, *Tyria jacobaeae*, on Tansy Ragwort in the Western United States. *J. econ. Ent.* **57**, 152–154.

Gause, G. F. (1934). "The Struggle for Existence", Williams & Wilkins, Baltimore.

Ghent, A. W. (1960). A study of the group-feeding of larvae of the jackpine sawfly, *Neodiprion pratti banksianae* Roh. *Behaviour* **16**, 110–148.

Gibb, J. A. (1958). Predation by tits and squirrels on the eucosmid *Ernarmonia conicolana* (Heyl.). *J. Anim. Ecol.* **27**, 375–396.

Gibb, J. A. (1966). Tit predation and the abundance of *Ernarmonia conicolana* (Heyl.) on Weeting Heath, Norfolk, 1962–63. *J. Anim. Ecol.* **35**, 43–53.

Gruys, P. (1970). Growth in *Bupalus piniarius* (Lepidoptera: Geometridae) in relation to larval population density. *Verh. Rijksinst. Natuurbeheer* **1**, 1–127.

Gulland, J. A. (1971). The effect of exploitation on the numbers of marine mammals. *In* "Dynamics of Populations" (P. J. den Boer and G. R. Gradwell, eds.), pp. 450–468. Centre for Agricultural Publishing and Documentation, Wageningen.

Hancock, D. A. (1969). An experiment with overcrowded cockles (*Cardium edule* L.). Proc. Symp. Mollusca (Cochin 12–16 Jan. 1968) Symposium Ser. 3, Pt. II, Marine biol. Ass. India Symp. Ser. 3. Mandapam Camp, India, pp. 396–402.

Hancock, D. A. (1971). The role of predators and parasites in a fishery for the mollusc *Cardium edule* L. *In* "Dynamics of Populations" (P. J. den Boer and G. R. Gradwell, eds.), pp. 419–439. Centre for Agricultural Publishing and Documentation, Wageningen.

Hancock, D. A. and Franklin, A. (1972). Seasonal changes in the condition of the edible cockle (*Cardium edule* L.). *J. appl. Ecol.* **9**, 567–579.

Hancock, D. A. and Urquhart, A. E. (1965). The determination of natural mortality and its causes in an exploited population of cockles (*Cardium edule* L.). *Fishery Invest., Lond.*, Ser. II, **24**, 1–40.

Harding, D. and Talbot, J. W. (1973). Recent studies on the eggs and larvae of the plaice (*Pleuronectes platessa* L.) in the Southern Bight. *Rapp. P.-v. Réun. Cons. perm. int. Explor. Mer.* **164**, 261–269.

Harper, J. L. and Wood, W. A. (1957). Biological flora of the British Isles, *Senecio jacobaea* L. *J. Ecol.* **45**, 617–637.

Harris, P. (1973). Insects in the population dynamics of plants. *In* "Insect/Plant Relationships" (H. F. van Emden, ed.), pp. 201–208. Blackwell Scientific Publications, Oxford.

Hassell, M. P. (1966). Evaluation of parasite or predator responses. *J. Anim. Ecol.* **35**, 65–75.

Hawkes, R. B. (1968). The Cinnabar Moth, *Tyria jacobaeae*, for control of Tansey Ragwort. *J. econ. Ent.* **61**, 499–501.

Holling, C. S. (1959). The components of predation as revealed by a study of small mammal predation of the European pine sawfly. *Can. Ent.* **91**, 293–320.

Howard, H. E. (1920). "Territory in Bird Life", Murray, London.

Howard, L. O. and Fiske, W. F. (1911). The importation into the United States of the parasites of the gypsy-moth and the brown-tail moth. *Bull. Bur. Ent. U.S. Dep. Agric.* **91**, 1–312.

Hudleston, J. A. (1958). Some notes on the effects of bird predators on hopper bands of the Desert Locust (*Schistocerca gregaria* Forsk.). *Entomologists mon. Mag.* **94**, 210–214.

Hueck, H. J., Kuenen, D. J., den Boer, P. J. and Jaeger-Draafsel, E. (1952). The increase of egg production of the fruit tree red spider mite (*Metatetranychus ulmi* Koch.) under the influence of DDT. *Physiologia comp. Oecol.* **2**, 371–377.

Itô, Y. (1959). A comparative study on survivorship curves for natural insect populations. *Jap. J. Ecol.* **9**, 107–115.

Itô, Y. (1961). Factors that affect the fluctuations of animal numbers with special reference to insect outbreaks. *Bull. natn. Inst. agric. Sci., Tokyo*, Ser. C., **13**, 57–89.

Itô, Y. (1972). On the methods for determining density-dependence by means of regression. *Oecologia* **10**, 347–372.

Iwao, S. and Wellington, W. G. (1970). The western tent caterpillar: qualitative differences and the action of natural enemies. *Researches Popul. Ecol.* **12**, 81–99.

Jenkins, D., Watson, A. and Miller, G. R. (1963). Population studies on red grouse, *Lagopus lagopus scoticus* (Lath.) in north-east Scotland. *J. Anim. Ecol.* **32**, 317–376.

Jenkins, D., Watson, A. and Miller, G. R. (1967). Population fluctuations in the red grouse, *Lagopus lagopus scoticus. J. Anim. Ecol.* **36**, 97–122.

Johnson, C. G. (1960). A basis for a general system of insect migration and dispersal by flight. *Nature, Lond.*, **186**, 348–350.

Johnson, C. G. (1963). Physiological factors in insect migration by flight. *Nature, Lond.*, **198**, 423–427.

Keith, L. B. (1963). "Wildlife's Ten-Year Cycle", University of Wisconsin Press, Madison.

Kennedy, J. S. (1956). Phase transformation in locust biology. *Biol. Rev.* **31**, 349–370.

Kennedy, J. S. (1961). Continuous polymorphism in locusts. *In* "Insect Polymorphism" (J. S. Kennedy, ed.), Symposium No. 1, R. ent. Soc. Lond., pp. 80–90.

Key, K. H. L. (1950). A critique on the phases of locusts. *Q. Rev. Biol.* **25**, 363–407.

Klomp, H. (1965). The dynamics of a field population of the Pine Looper (*Bupalus piniarius* L.) (Lepidoptera: Geometridae). *Adv. Ecol. Res.* **3**, 207–305.

Korringa, P. (1971). Human intervention in the aquatic environment. *In* "Dynamics of Populations" (P. J. den Boer and G. R. Gradwell, eds.), pp. 440–449. Centre for Agricultural Publishing and Documentation, Wageningen.

Krebs, J. R. (1970). Regulation of numbers of the Great Tit (Aves: Passeriformes). *J. Zool.* **162**, 317–333.

Krebs, J. R. (1971). Territory and breeding density in the great tit, *Parus major* L. *Ecology* **52**, 2–22.

Kristensen, I. (1957). Differences in density and growth in a cockle population in the Dutch Wadden Sea. *Archs néerl. Zool.* **12**, 351–453.

Kuno, E. (1971). Sampling error as a misleading artifact in "key factor analysis". *Researches Popul. Ecol.* **8**, 28—45.

Lack, D. (1943). The age of some more British birds. *Br. Birds* **36**, 214–221.

Lack, D. (1966). "Population Studies of Birds". Claredon Press, Oxford.

Laws, R. M. (1962). Some effects of whaling on the southern stocks of baleen whales. *In* "The Exploitation of Natural Animal Populations" (E. D. Le Cren and M. W. Holdgate, eds.), pp. 137–158. Blackwell Scientific Publications, Oxford.

Lockie, J. D. (1955). The breeding habits and food of short-eared owls after a vole plaque. *Bird Study* **2**, 53–69.

Lotka, A. J. (1925). "Elements of Physical Biology". Williams & Wilkins, Baltimore.

Luck, R. F. (1971). An appraisal of two methods of analysing insect life tables. *Can. Ent.* **103**, 1261–1271.

Mackenzie, J. M. D. (1952). Fluctuations in the numbers of British tetraonids. *J. Anim. Ecol.* **21**, 128–153.

MacLagan, D. S. (1940). Sunspots and insect outbreaks: an epidemiological study. *Proc. Univ. Durham phil. Soc.* **10**, 173–199.

MacLulich, D. A. (1937). Fluctuations in the numbers of the varying hare (*Lepus americanus*). *Univ. Toronto Stud. biol. Ser.* No. 43, 5–136.

Maelzer, D. A. (1970). The regression of log. N_{n+1} on log. N_n as a test of density dependence: an exercise with computer-constructed density-independent populations. *Ecology* **51**, 810–822.

Mann, K. H. (1957). The breeding, growth and age structure of a population of the leech, *Helobdella stagnalis* L. *J. Anim. Ecol.* **26**, 171–177.

Merton, L. F. H. (1959). Studies on the ecology of the Moroccan Locust (*Dociostaurus maroccanus* Thunberg) in Cyprus. *Anti-Locust Bull.* **34**, 1–123.

Milne, A. (1957a). Theories of natural control of insect populations. *Cold Spring Harb. Symp. quant. Biol.* **22**, 253–271.

Milne, A. (1957b). The natural control of insect populations. *Can. Ent.* **89**, 193–213.

Milne, A. (1961). Definition of competition among animals. *Symp. Soc. exp. Biol.* **15**, 40–71.

Milne, A. (1962). On a theory of natural control of insect populations. *J. theor. Biol.* **3**, 19–50.

Moore, N. W. (1964). Intra and interspecific competition among dragonflies (Odonata). *J. Anim. Ecol.* **33**, 49–71.

References

Morris, R. F. (1959). Single factor analysis in population dynamics. *Ecology* **40**, 580–588.

Moss, R. (1969). A comparison of red grouse (*Lagopus l. scoticus*) stocks with the production and nutritive value of heather (*Caluna vulgaris*). *J. Anim. Ecol.* **38**, 103–112.

Mueller, H. C. (1973). The relationship of hunger to predatory behaviour in hawks (*Falco sparvarius* and *Buteo playpterus*). *Anim. Behav.* **21**, 513–520.

Murie, A. (1944). The Wolves of Mt. McKinley. *Fauna natn. Pks. U.S.*, No. 5.

Murton, R. K. (1961). Some survival estimates for the Woodpigeon. *Bird Study* **8**, 165–173.

Murton, R. K. (1965). "The Wood-Pigeon", Collins, London.

Murton, R. K. (1971). The significance of a specific search image in the feeding behaviour of the wood pigeon. *Behaviour* **40**, 10–42.

Murton, R. K. (1973). The decline of the woodpigeon. *Shooting Times and Country Magazine*. Oct. 27. pp. 21–22.

Murton, R. K. (1974a). The impact of agriculture on birds. *Ann. appl. Biol.* **76**, 34–42.

Murton, R. K. (1974b). "Avian Breeding Cycles", Clarendon Press, Oxford.

Murton, R. K., Isaacson, A. J. and Westwood, N. J. (1966). The relationships between wood pigeons and their clover food supply and the mechanism of population control. *J. appl. Ecol.* **3**, 55–96.

Murton, R. K., Isaacson, A. J. and Westwood, N. J. (1971). The significance of gregarious feeding behaviour and adrenal stress in a population of wood-pigeons, *Columba palumbus. J. Zool.* **165**, 53–84.

Murton, R. K., Westwood, N. J. and Isaacson, A. J. (1974). A study of wood-pigeon shooting: the exploitation of a natural animal population. *J. appl. Ecol.* **11**, 61–81.

Nicholson, A. J. (1933). The balance of animal populations. *J. Anim. Ecol.* **2**, suppl. 1, 132–178.

Nicholson, A. J. (1954). An outline of the dynamics of animal populations. *Aust. J. Zool.* **2**, 9–65.

Nicholson, A. J. (1957). The self-adjustment of populations to change. *Cold Spring Harb. Symp. quant. Biol.* **22**, 153–173.

Nicholson, A. J. (1958). Dynamics of insect populations. *A. Rev. Ent.* **3**, 107–136.

Nicholson, A. J. and Bailey, V. A. (1935). The balance of animal populations, Part I. *Proc. zool. Soc., Lond.* Pt. 3, 551–598.

Park, T. (1948). Experimental studies of interspecies competition. I. Competition between populations of flour beetles *Tribolium confusum* Duval and *T. castaneum* Herbst. *Ecol. Monogr.* **18**, 265–308.

Parrish, B. B. (1956). The cod, haddock and hake. *In* "Sea Fisheries, Their Investigation in the United Kingdom" (M. Graham, ed.) pp. 251–331. Edward Arnold, London.

Pimental, D. (1961). Animal population regulation by the genetic feed-back mechanism. *Am. Nat.* **95**, 65–79.

Pitelka, F. A., Tomich, P. Q. and Treichel, G. W. (1955). Ecological relations of jaegers and owls as lemming predators near Barrow, Alaska. *Ecol. Monogr.* **25,** 85–117.

Recher, H. F. and Recher, J. A. (1969). Some aspects of the ecology of migrant shorebirds. II aggression. *Wilson Bull.* **81,** 140–154.

Reynoldson, T. B. and Bellamy, L. S. (1971). The establishment of inter-specific competition in field populations, with an example of competition in action between *Polycelis nigra* (Mull.) and *P. tenuis* (Ijima) (Turbellaria, Tricladida). *In* "Dynamics of Populations" (P. J. den Boer and G. R. Gradwell, eds.), pp. 282–297. Centre for Agricultural Publishing and Documentation, Wageningen.

Reynoldson, T. B. and Davies, R. W. (1970). Food niche and co-existence in lake-dwelling triclads. *J. Anim. Ecol.* **39,** 599–617.

Richards, O. W. and Waloff, N. (1961). A study of a natural population of *Phytodecta olivacea* (Forster) (Coleoptera, Chrysomeloidea). *Phil. Trans. R. Soc.*, Ser. B, **244,** 205–257.

Sheail, J. (1971). "Rabbits and Their History". David & Charles, Newton Abbot.

Shields, O. (1967). Hilltopping: an ecological study of summit congregation behaviour of Lepidoptera in Southern California. *J. Res. Lepid.* **6,** 71–178.

Siivonen, L. (1948). Structure of short-cyclic fluctuations in numbers of mammals and birds in the northern parts of the northern hemisphere. *Riistat. Julk.* **1,** 1–66.

Smith, H. S. (1935). The role of biotic factors in the determination of population densities. *J. econ. Ent.* **28,** 873–898.

Smith, K. D. and Popov, G. B. (1953). On birds attacking Desert Locust swarms in Eritrea. *Entomologist* **86,** 3–7.

Smith, R. H. (1973). The analysis of inter-generation change in animal populations. *J. Anim. Ecol.* **42,** 611–622.

Solomon, M. E. (1949). The natural control of animal populations. *J. Anim. Ecol.* **18,** 1–35.

Solomon, M. E. (1964). Analysis of processes involved in the natural control of insects. *Adv. Ecol. Res.* **2,** 1–58.

Southern, H. N. (1954). Tawny owls and their prey. *Ibis* **96,** 384–410.

Southern, H. N. (1970). The natural control of a population of Tawny owls (*Strix aluco*). *J. Zool.* **162,** 197–285.

Southwood, T. R. E. (1962). Migration of terrestrial arthropods in relation to habitat. *Biol. Rev.* **37,** 171–214.

Southwood, T. R. E. (1966). "Ecological Methods: With Particular Reference to the Study of Insect Populations", Methuen, London.

Stafford, J. (1971). Heron populations of England and Wales 1928–70. *Bird Study* **18,** 218–221.

St. Amant, J. L. (1970). The detection of regulation in animal populations. *Ecology* **51,** 823–828.

Tansley, A. G. (1935). The use and abuse of vegetational concepts and terms. *Ecology* **16,** 284–307.

Tinbergen, L. (1960). The natural control of insects in pinewoods. I. Factors influencing the intensity of predation by songbirds. *Archs néerl. Zool.* **13,** 265–343.

Ullyett, G. C. (1949a). Distribution of progeny by *Chelonus texanus* Cress. (Hymenoptera, Braconidae). *Can. Ent.* **81,** 25–44.

Ullyett, G. C. (1949b). Distribution of progeny by *Cryptis inornatus* Pratt. (Hymenoptera: Ichneumonidae). *Can. Ent.* **81,** 285–299.

Uvarov, B. P. (1921). A revision of the genus *Locusta* L. (= *Pachytylus* Fieb.), with a new theory as to the periodicity and migrations of locusts. *Bull. ent. Res.* **12,** 135–163.

Uvarov, B. P. (1931). Insects and climate. *Trans. R. ent. Soc. Lond.* **79,** 1–247.

Uvarov, B. P. (1961). Quantity and quality in insect populations. *Proc. R. ent. Soc. Lond.*, Ser. C. **25,** 52–59.

Uvarov, B. P. (1964). Problems of insect ecology in developing countries. *J. appl. Ecol.* **1,** 159–168.

Uvarov, B. P. (1966). "Grasshoppers and Locusts. A Handbook of General Acridology, Vol. 1". Cambridge University Press, London.

Varley, G. C. (1947). The natural control of population balance in the knapweed gall-fly (*Urophora jaceana*). *J. Anim. Ecol.* **16,** 139–189.

Varley, G. C. (1949). Population changes in German forest pests. *J. Anim. Ecol.* **18,** 117–122.

Varley, G. C. and Gradwell, G. R. (1960). Key factors in population studies. *J. Anim. Ecol.* **29,** 399–401.

Varley, G. C. and Gradwell, G. R. (1963). The interpretation of insect population changes. *Proc. Ceylon Ass. Advnt Sci., 18th Annual Session,* Part II, 142–156.

Varley, G. C. and Gradwell, G. R. (1968). Population models for the Winter Moth. *In* "Insect Abundance" (T. R. E. Southwood, ed.), pp. 132–142. Blackwell Scientific Publications, Oxford.

Volterra, V. (1926). Variazioni e fluttuazioni del numero d'individui in specie animali conviventi. *Atti. Accad. naz. Lincei Memorie* Ser. 6, **2,** 31–113. (English translation in R. N. Chapman, 1931, "Animal Ecology". pp. 409–448, McGraw-Hill, New York).

Waloff, N. (1967). Biology of three species of *Leiophron* (Hymenoptera: Braconidae, Eulophorinae) parasitic on Miridae on broom. *Trans. R. ent. Soc. Lond.* **119,** 187–213.

Waloff, N. and Richards, O. W. (1958). The biology of the chrysomelid beetle *Phytodecta olivacea* (Forster) (Coleoptera: Chrysomelidae). *Trans. R. ent. Soc. Lond.* **110,** 99–116.

Watmough, R. H. (1968). Population studies on two species of Psyllidae (Homoptera: Sternorhyncha) on broom (*Sarothamnus scoparius* (L) Wimmer). *J. Anim. Ecol.* **37,** 283–314.

Watson, A. (1971). Key factor analysis, density dependence and population limitation in red grouse. *In* "Dynamics of Populations" (P. J. den Boer and G. R. Gradwell, eds.). pp. 548–564. Centre for Agricultural Publishing and Documentation, Wageningen.

Watson, A. and Miller, G. R. (1971). Territory size and aggression in a fluctuating red grouse population. *J. Anim. Ecol.* **40,** 367–383.

Watson, A. and Moss, R. (1972). A current model of population dynamics in red grouse. *Int. orn. Congr.* 15. The Hague 1970, 134–149.

Way, M. J. (1968). Intra-specific mechanisms with special reference to aphid populations. *In* "Insect Abundance" (T. R. E. Southwood, ed.). pp. 18–36. Blackwell Scientific Publications, Oxford.

Way, M. J. and Cammell, M. E. (1971). Self regulation in aphid populations. *In* "Dynamics of Populations" (P. J. den Boer and G. R. Gradwell, eds.). pp. 232–242. Centre for Agricultural Publishing and Documentation, Wageningen.

Weeden, R. B. and Theberge, J. B. (1972). The dynamics of a fluctuating population of Rock Ptarmigan in Alaska. *Int. orn. Congr.* 15. The Hague 1970, 90–106.

Wellington, W. G. (1957). Individual differences as a factor in population dynamics: the development of a problem. *Can. J. Zool.* **35,** 293–323.

Wellington, W. G. (1960). Qualitative changes in natural populations during changes in abundance. *Can. J. Zool.* **38,** 289–314.

Wellington, W. G. (1962). Population quality and the maintenance of nuclear polyhedrosis between outbreaks of *Malacosoma pluviale* (Dyar). *J. Insect Path.* **4,** 285–305.

Wellington, W. G. (1964). Qualitative changes in populations in unstable environments. *Can. Ent.* **96,** 436–451.

Wilkinson, A. T. S. (1965). Releases of Cinnabar moth (*Hypocrita jacobaeae* L.) on tansy ragwort in British Columbia. *Proc. ent. Soc. Br. Columb.* **62,** 10–12.

Williams, G. R. (1954). Population fluctuations in some northern hemisphere game birds (Tetraonidae). *J. Anim. Ecol.* **23,** 1–34.

Williamson, M. (1972). "The Analysis of Biological Populations". Edward Arnold, London.

Wylie, H. G. (1966). Some mechanisms that affect the sex ratio of *Nasonia vitripennis* (Walk.) (Hymenoptera: Pteromalidae) reared from super-parasitized housefly pupae. *Can. Ent.* **98,** 645–653.

Wynne-Edwards, V. C. (1962). "Animal Dispersion in Relation to Social Behaviour". Oliver & Boyd, Edinburgh and London.

Subject Index

153